A Pirate's Guide t' th' Grammar of Story

A Creative Writing Curriculum
By Yogger LeFossa

Wondertale
Newt Yorker, Vangroover, Lungdon, Instantbul, Toykeyo

A Pirate's Guide t' th' Grammar of Story: A Creative Writing Curriculum
Copyright © 2016 by Christopher R. Hansen
All Rights Reserved. Published 2016
First Edition, May 2016

Authors: S. Christopher Hansen and J.R. Fehr
Cover Art: S. Christopher Hansen
Publisher: Wondertale

ISBN-10: 1-945353-00-7
ISBN-13: 978-1-945353-00-0

Wondertale
California, USA

TABLE OF CONTENTS

The Grammar of Story

<u>Grammar</u>: the basic elements of an area of knowledge or skill.

Exercise #1 – <u>Mindstorming</u>: An exercise to help a storyteller come up with ideas.

Exercise #2 – <u>Being Specific</u>: Being specific is a way of setting limits and creating a focus.

Exercise #3 – <u>Setting</u>: Setting is the time and place where this story takes place; establishing time and place is one way to give your story world some boundaries.

Exercise #4 – <u>Values</u>: Values are things that are valuable.

Exercise #5 – <u>Significance</u>: To be significant is to be worthy of attention.

Exercise #6 – <u>Rules</u>: Rules help define what can and cannot happen in the story world. Rules govern behavior within the story world.

Exercise #7 – <u>Symbols</u>: A symbol represents something. It stands in the place of something else. Symbols communicate complex things in simple ways.

Exercise #8 – <u>Backstory</u>: In story, the string of events that took place in the past is called a backstory; it is the story that led up to the story being told, and it explains why things are as they are in the story world.

Exercise #9 – <u>Connections</u>: Connections are all the ways different parts of a story come together.

Exercise #10 – <u>Problems and the Act of Villainy</u>: An Act of Villainy is a problem that causes one or more characters to respond to try and solve it.

Exercise #11 – <u>Characterizations</u>: Characterizations describe things. These descriptions give details that define who or what a character is.

Exercise #12 – <u>Characterizations, Part Two</u>: The process of creating a character is called character design.

Exercise #13 – <u>Character Values</u>: Character values are the things that are valuable to characters.

Exercise #14 – <u>The Line Between Light and Dark</u>: For all characters, the Act of Villainy becomes a dividing line that separates them onto two different sides.

Exercise #15 – <u>Mystery</u>: Mystery fuels our curiosity; it captures our attention and keeps us engaged. Mystery isn't essential for a story, but makes it more gripping.

Exercise #16 – <u>Character Contradictions</u>: Characters don't always make sense; they can have contradictions.

Exercise #17 – <u>Character Desire</u>: Desires identify what a character wants.

<u>Stakes</u>: What is at risk if a character does not achieve their desire.

<u>Ticking Clock</u>: The pressure on a character to accomplish their desire before time runs out.

Exercise #18 – <u>Story Engine</u>: Characters are the story engine; characters are the engine of every story.

Intro to Character Function: <u>Character functions</u> describe the role a character plays in a story, based on who they are (characterizations), what they want (desires), the choices they make (story engine), and the actions they take (plot).

Exercise #19 – Princess and Villain:

<u>Villain</u>: a character/thing that is on the side of the Act of Villainy.

<u>Princess</u>: a character/thing being fought over.

Exercise #20 – Dispatch and Hero:

<u>Hero</u>: a character/thing that liquidates (solves) the Act of Villainy.

<u>Dispatcher</u>: a character/thing that informs the Hero there is a problem to be solved.

Exercise #21 – Donor and Magical Agent:

<u>Donor</u>: a character/thing that connects the Hero to the Magical Agent.

<u>Magical Agent</u>: a character/thing that is needed to liquidate (solves) the Act of Villainy.

Exercise #22 – Helper and King:

<u>Helper</u>: a character/thing that contributes to the liquidation of the Act of Villainy.

<u>King</u>: the King is the sovereign over the thing being fought over (the Princess).

Exercise #23 – <u>Plot</u>: Plot is a series of events that occur one after another.

Exercise #24 – <u>Gaps and Expectation</u>: When a character expects things will go one way and then discovers they're going another, we call it a gap.

Exercise #25 – <u>Beginning, Middle, End</u>: Thinking in terms of beginning, middle and end can help you organize all of the events that happen in a story.

Exercise #26 – <u>Transformation</u>: The things that change because of the actions of the characters.

<u>Character Arc</u>: The transformation that takes place in a character over the course of a story.

CHAPTER AYE

One minute, you're closing your eyes and drifting into a nice, peaceful sleep, the next, you're surrounded by a torrent of raging water and being violently whisked down a dark tunnel.

You struggle to slow your spinning and grab for something – anything! – that might slow you down or help, but nothing does and you continue to slide through the darkness.

"Where am I!?" you want to scream, but can't, because every time you try to open your mouth, it fills with warm, salty water.

As you spin and thrash around, you feel like someone has literally flushed you down a massive toilet.

"This is the end!" you think, as you realize you can't hold your breath any longer, when all of a sudden. . .

. . .you are shot straight out of what would be the scariest waterslide in the world and are launched into the dark, stormy sky.

You soar up, higher and higher, until your ascent gradually slows and – like a character in a cartoon – you hover in the sky.

All around you, for miles and miles, is a beautiful sea – far brighter and bluer than any sea you've ever seen before. It extends as far as you can see in every direction.

You want to stay here and admire the view for longer, but then gravity decides to come back from lunch break and all at once you're tumbling helplessly back down to the sea.

"Ahhhhhhhhhhhhh!" you scream as you shut your eyes.

You expect to feel your body painfully smash into the water beneath you, but instead, you're caught by something soft that significantly slows your fall.

"Ahoy!" A deep and friendly voice calls out to you.

You open your eyes and see you're now inside a large fishing net and are being dragged through the waves to an incredibly large, wooden ship in motion. You've never seen anything like it before: it's carved of elegant, dark wood with portholes along the side that contain row upon row of cannons, and has two large, towering masts that for some reason fly no sails. How this ship manages to move anywhere is a complete mystery to you.

Once to the ship, you do your best to scramble up the side, but continually slip down until a strong hand reaches down and helps pull you up.

As soon as you're onboard, you roll onto your back and break into a fit of gagging and wheezing; you've never been so scared in your entire life!

"Thanks," you manage to say once you finally catch your breath.

"Th' pleasure be mine, mate," a gruff voice replies.

As your strength starts to return, you manage to stand back on your feet. But what you see next shocks you so badly, you nearly fall back down; you're standing on the deck of a massive pirate ship!

You know it must be a pirate ship, because standing right in front of you is an evil-looking pirate.

You assume the pirate must be the captain because he's wearing a black pirate coat trimmed in a bright orange color, complete with a tri-cornered hat on his head. Like you'd expect of a pirate captain, he's got a long, black beard, a patch over his left eye, not just one but two peg legs, and a hook for a left hand.

You stare intently at him and wonder how you possibly came to be here and if this pirate is going to harm you or not.

Thankfully, you don't have to worry for long, because as soon as you make eye contact, a smile spreads across his face and he flashes you a golden toothed grin as he pulls a green jelly bean out of his pocket and pops it into his mouth.

"Avast there, matey! Welcome aboard!"

You can't quite tell if he's safe or not, but decide to be as polite as possible in the hope he'll have mercy on you.

"I'm sorry," you stumble to find the words, "but . . . where am I?"

"We be in th' middle o' th' Pancific Ocean!"

You stare at him blankly.

"Do you mean the Pacific Ocean?"

The captain scrunches his eyebrows together.

"What? Nar, nar, Pancific, mate!"

You scratch the back of your head and wonder if it's a slur because of his accent.

"Are you . . . a real pirate?" you ask timidly.

None of this makes any sense. Pirates like this only exist in stories, or so you thought.

The captain stares at you with wild curiosity, then grabs his belly and bursts into jovial laughter.

"Yo ho ho! Not just any pirate! Yer lookin' at th' fearsome Yogger LeFossa, scourge o' th' Emerald Island, lover o' story, an' subduer of sea monsters. What say ye be yer name?"

(Ye best be writin' yer name here, if ye know how!)

_____

As soon as you say your name, Captain Yogger breaks into gregarious laughter. The stench of his hot, foul breath is almost more than you can take, and you do everything in your power to resist taking a step away for fear of offending him.

"Ya har! That name be more suited fer a seagull than a landlubber child like ye. Har har! From now on, ye be called Scurvy Spat, 'cause ye be spat out o' th' ocean like a disease! Har!"

You don't exactly love the sound of your new name, but you don't think you have much of a choice in the matter.

"Thanks, I guess," you mumble.

Just then, you hear a chorus of laughter behind you, and turn around to see the ship is full of tiny monkeys dressed like pirates. Some wear vests and bandanas, others jackets and hats, but all of them wear black pants and carry curved swords.

"Aye! Thar be me monkey mates! Mates, say 'ello to Scurvy Spat!"

The monkeys jump up and down and wave their arms in the air, chanting your name and laughing at the same time. It's one of the most bizarre things you've ever seen.

They dance their way closer to you, causing you wrinkle your nose in disgust. You thought the captain had bad breath, but it's nothing compared to the smell of these monkeys.

"Enough!" Captain Yogger shouts abruptly, and the laughter immediately stops. "Get back t' werk, ye pox-faced, lice-infested, free bootin' scoundrels! We gots us a treasure t' be findin'!"

The monkeys scatter at the sound of his voice. Once gone, the pirate turns his back to you and pulls what looks like a map out of his pocket.

You take a step toward him to get a better look. It appears very old and worn and is made out of some thick material, like leather. You can't see much more than a dotted line travelling past many islands and creatures that might be sea serpents. But, at the end of the line and in the middle of the sea, one mark catches your eye: a big red "X."

If you're really on a pirate ship, this has got to be a treasure map.

A letter from the desk of the notorious Pirate Captain Yogger LeFossa.

T' whoever be th' parental guardian of this here child:

Seein' as I kidnapped yer lil' one, it be only fittin' that I send ye a letter. Me mother, th' Queen of th' Emerald Isle, were strict wit' me 'bout sendin' thank-ye notes. So, before I start wit' turnin' yer offspring into a infamous pirate, I wanted t' spend a moment t' say how much I value th' opportunity you've given me t' take possession of yer spawn.

Since yer wee precious jewel will be a captive on me ship, me thinks a proper introduction be in order. It be only polite fer a parent t' know something 'bout who'll be indoctrinatin' their progeny. I be Captain Yogger LeFossa, scourge o' th' Emerald Island, lover o' story, an' subduer of sea monsters. I demand a clean, orderly ship, an' fer everyone on it t' do the work set before them. Swabbin' decks all day and keepin' watch through th' foggy night be tedious work fer some. Any who are not bein' up to thar job be free t' jump overboard anytime thay see fit.

We be story makin' pirates, and it be our job now t' train up yer little urchin in our ways. But, they need t' be doin' their part if thay be knowin' what be good fer 'em. This ain't some smooth sailing algebra or calculus doodlin' work, nor some sissy study in civics. Yer spawn be needin' t' labor t' make it through th' slog we'll be puttin' them through. If thay don't cry out in agony because of all th' drudgery, then we failed in our duty t' train them. It ain't easy becomin' a story-makin' pirate; not many get t' th' end and find th' treasure thay be lookin' fer.

Ye should also know yer tiny trooper will most likely break down and whine like a baby monkey, sayin', "This be too hard," "I can't do this," or "Why do I have to do every exercise?" Of course it be hard! Most likely thay be tryin' t' get out of doing th' work we have fer them. Don't worry, many kids be playin' these games an' we just be doin' what works best. A couple lashes with the cat o' nine tales – har har – usually get's 'em back in line. That, or th' plank.

Ya har! I only be kiddin'. Th' way t' train up a storyteller is t' encourage creativity. This means thar can't be any pressure. We never make someone walk th' plank if thay do thar work. Thar bein' no good or bad, 'cause thar no grades, no expectations, no comparin' thar work t' anyone else. Yer lil' childin can be as dull as me peg lega an' have th' creativity of th' hair on a gnat an' that be just fine wit' us.

Don't fret yer precious little un's head, we won't be pushin' them past their limits. Creative werk can be exhausting, after all! One o' th' first things we be figurin' out is how much werk each youngin' can be doin' in one sittin' before their noggin' be turned to smashed carp! We start yer critters werkin' fer 20 minutes two ter three times per week an' see how they be survivin' before attachin' more time. An' if thay ever be feelin' faint, we just let em' fall out o' thar chair an' take a lil' nap. It be a little known secret that story makin' pirates enjoy a good nap now and again.

Criticism be like a storm that sinks thar brain ship. But don't be fooled – praise can be as deadly as sharpenin' yer sword with a krakens tooth. So ye won't be seein' us give out no magical gold stars or blue ribbons or any o' that thar landlubber stuff that be fillin' a youngin's head wit' nonsense. We just have 'em do thar work an' laugh an' dance an' play along. Nothin' quite as much fun as creativity, ya har!

Don't be afeared, I be understandin' that ev'ry child be different. I trained quite a few in me day. Fer one child, a section might feel t' them like baby work, but fer another, it be makin' them jump aroun' like thay be on fire. Another might feel some parts be impossible. Fer these exercises, we may be needin' t' hold thar hand an' help 'em make it through what t' them seems like a storm. This be a time t' slow down, stay calm, and help 'em keep thar head. Bein' creative at times will scare th' wits out of even hard worn pirate captains like me.

But, if thay get stuck, we'll not be ever doin' th' work fer them. That be sinkin' creativity like a cannon ball in yer hull. That be teachin' them thay can't be doin' it, or thay be better leavin' it t' someone more experienced than them. Pollywogs!

Creativity is not like building a ship. Thar ain't one right answer; fictional stories can't be right o' wrong. They be more like flowers that need t' be opened before one can see th' beautiful colors that be inside.

I need t' repeat: we no be doin' any good by doin' th' work fer them. We don't be givin' them ideas, we let 'em come up with thar own. I know th' itch t' do th' work myself – I have a crew of monkeys, fer cryin' out loud! So, whenever I be feelin' this way, I grab me a paper o' me own an' do th' work right beside me captives. Some of me best laughs be had sharin' work. Fer this reason, I always prefer t' have me captives do thar work wit' others in groups.

We also be focusin' on each captive's responses. We listen t' thar creativity. Reading yer sea squirrels responses be like uncoverin' buried treasure. Th' stories that come out of someone will tell ye all kinds of tales about that person. Most kids are desperate t' tell us each and every one of th' things thay wrote down. Listening without makin' comments be openin' them up.

Last, we be story makin' pirates, not because we be lovin' stories, but 'cause we love life itself. Everything we'll do t' try and wash yer little grub's mind is meant t' help them write th' story of thar life. We only be gettin' one life story t' write. We can write a boring one, or one full o' life. That be why we chose t' kidnapped yer kid and set sail wit' them on an adventure we hope will be terrific fun fer us all.

And if it isn't, thar always be th' plank.

Th' one an' only,
Captain Yogger LeFossa

IMPORTANT NOTE FROM THE PUBLISHER
If you, like us, think the contents of this "letter" utterly impossible to understand, please turn to page 322, at the back of the book, where we have placed our properly written introduction and instructions for parents and teachers.

(Kids, make sure your parents read this.)

CHAPTER AYE AYE

"Whoa! Is that a treasure map?" you ask, as you try to peek around Captain Yogger's thick frame.

"Avast!" He spins around and folds up the map before you can see much. "Ye best be careful. I ne'er said ye were me crew yet, now did I?"

His words send a chill down your spine.

"Um, I guess not."

Captain Yogger eyes you suspiciously.

"Things be a lil' different on me ship than that o' other capt'n's. Any mates be welcome t' join me on me quest if thay be willin' t' put th' werk in." Captain Yogger pops a jelly bean into his mouth.

"What kind of work?"

"Hard werk. Livin' on the sea be no place for landlubbers."

You swallow hard as you wonder what he means.

"Everyone need t' be doing their part t' take care o' me ship. Bein' that yer new, ye be starting out wit' the easy stuff, like swabbin' decks, night watch, and otherwise doin' everything yer commanded."

Easy stuff? You thought he said it would be hard work.

"Takin' care o' me ship be easy, if everyone be doin' thar part. The hard werk be comin' from th' fact that we be story-makin' pirates."

"Story-making pirates?" You don't understand. "Do you mean you tell stories?"

"Aye, and write 'em and dance 'em and sing 'em. But, most important, we live 'em."

You certainly don't understand this. But, you like stories. You always have.

"Do ye want t' be makin' stories, Scurvy Spat?"

"Yes, I've always wanted to do that."

"Then ye found yerself th' right ship, har har!" His loud laugh belts out across the ship.

"Do you teach people about stories?"

"So far I only be teachin' me monkeys 'bout story. But, it seems t' be about time I be venturin' out with humans. So, are ye ready t' be werkin' hard, human?"

Learning about stories doesn't seem that bad; it shouldn't be as hard as all the other stuff you have to learn in school. So, you say, "I guess."

Captain Yogger eyes you with suspicion. "This ship ain't th' lovey-dovey, yer-so-special-cause-ye-can-spell-yer-own-name type o' place. We won't be pinchin' yer sweet lil' cheek fer ev'ry tiny thing ye do. If ye be wantin' all that flowery mumbo-jumbo, ye may as well go find yerself another capt'n. Cause' on me ship, ye be learning 'bout th' Grammar o' Story."

What? The Grammar of Story. That sounds awful. Who wants to be trapped on a ship full of monkeys learning grammar? You suddenly feel sea sick and stagger over to the railing of the ship.

"Ye don't have t' be stayin' here, Scurvy Spat. Ye can be taking' a leap overboard an' go back into th' sea from whence ye came."

That doesn't seem like a good option.

"Ye be understandin' what I mean by Grammar, aye?"

"Sure, it's all the boring rules you have to learn if you want to write a proper sentence."

"Ya har! An' th' Grammar o' Story be all th' borin' stuff ye have t' learn if ye want t' be tellin' exhilaratin' stories."

You can't tell if he is being serious or not.

"I'll not be lying t' ye, Spat. Story makin' be hard werk, an' a lot o' it will be as excitin' as swabbin' th' deck. But, some will be fun and ye'll feel like me monkeys when thay be up on th' deck, jumpin' and holleran' and dancin' and laughin'."

"But, why Grammar? Can't I just learn how to write stories?"

"Th' Grammar o' Story be the best way t' start learnin' story. If ye want to be makin' a ship, ye need t' introduce yerself t' all th' basic elements that go into it: hulls, decks, masts, wheels, and rudders. Ye need t' know about salt water, kraken, zephyrs, and cannonballs. All this be th' grammar o' a ship."

"That doesn't sound anything like the grammar I was taught."

"Ya har! Grammar most oft' be a word used t' torture students."

"Then why do you use it?"

"I be a pirate, I like lootin', plunderin', an' torturin'," the captain says with a wink. Again, you can't tell if he is being serious or not. "Nar, nar, relax yer noggin'. It only be because o' how I be raised. When I were an urchin like yerself, I had me one o' them golden spoon classical educations, and I were tortured with Grammar, Logic, and Rhetoric. So, now I be doin' my best job t' be afflicting the younger generations wit' th' same."

This doesn't sound good.

"Now, enough worthless talk. It's time ye be makin' yer choice, Scurvy Spat. Are ye willin' t' werk fer me, or do ye want t' walk th' plank and try yer luck with ol' Davie Jones at th' bottom o' th' sea?"

Though part of you is still afraid – and you desperately want to go home and be away from this pirate – you nod in agreement and hope that maybe you'll find something on the way that can help you get home.

"I . . . guess I don't have much of a choice," you admit nervously.

"That be an aye?" Captain Yogger pops another jelly bean into his mouth as the sound of thunder rumbles in the distance.

You take a deep breath and say, "Aye, Captain."

"Ye won't be regrettin' that decision. It be well worth your time t' be comin' with, and thar be much loot to be plunderin' on th' way. Now get down below and meet me First Mate, Manfred. He be needin' t' teach ye how to read th' map before we can be talkin' about th' treasure we seek. Off now, an' don't ye be botherin' me!"

At that, Captain Yogger LeFossa hobbles away to his private quarters. But, before he steps inside, he turns back and shouts, "Don't be forgettin' this be a pirate ship."

You don't think you'll ever be able to forget that.

CHAPTER AYE AYE AYE

You stumble down the stairs and into the lowest level of the ship. It's dark down here, and the only light comes from a few lanterns hanging on the walls. There is a strange smell you can't quite identify. You're beginning to wonder if you made the right choice in staying with the pirate, when all of a sudden:

"Yo ho!" A monkey with a pink bow on her head drops in front of your face and waves her arms back and forth as she hangs upside down by her tail.

"Ahhhh!" you let out a startled shriek. You've never seen a monkey this close before.

The monkey giggles, drops to the ground, and scampers away.

"That was Missy Monkey," a calm, refined, and very un-piratey voice explains from behind you, "if you're going to stay on this ship, you're going to have to get used to us monkeys."

"Who said that?" you ask as you spin around.

Standing at the top of the steps is a monkey dressed in a snug, golden vest, with a red banana bandana over his head. He descends the stairs and extends his furry hand to shake yours.

"I am First Mate Manfred. Pleased to meet you."

You're stunned. You knew there were monkeys in human clothing, but you didn't expect them to be able to speak English. Wherever you are, it's nothing like home.

"Nice to, uh, meet you," you reply. It feels strange to be talking to a monkey.

You notice right away that Manfred is taller than the other monkeys you've seen so far, and is covered with brown hair, flecked with grey. You wonder if the grey means he's older than the others.

Manfred beckons you to follow as he walks down the hallway and into a room.

You cautiously follow him, and as soon as you get to the door, you're hit with an overpowering odor; the room is filled with stinky monkeys squatting around a table.

"Attention, everyone! I'd like to introduce you to the newest member of our ship, Scurvy Spat."

If your nose could speak, it would be begging you to run away from the smell. But, running would be rude. And besides, these monkeys also seem to be pirates, and offending them could be quite dangerous.

You lean your head out the door, take a deep breath, and reluctantly enter the room.

"A human?" one of the monkeys grunts. "You Brintish? Or from Northern Canmerico?"

"I . . . uhh. . ." all the monkeys stare at you blankly and wait for a response.

(Fill in the blank to tell the monkeys where you're from.)

"Neither. I'm from _____."

The monkeys exchange confused looks with one another.

"That's not a place!" one of them pipes up.

"Yes, it is," you reply.

"No, it's not, Scurvy Spat!" the monkey with the pink bow giggles and points.

"Yes, it is," you answer rather defensively.

"OK, OK, no fighting on the ship," First Mate Manfred raises his hand and beckons you to take a seat at the table. "It's clear our friend is from some other world."

"Another world?" the monkeys murmur amongst themselves. "Is that possible?"

"It would appear so." First Mate Manfred turns to you. "You look a little uneasy, Spat. Do you have talking monkeys where you're from?"

"Umm . . . well . . no. . ." you reply.

The monkeys stare at you for a few seconds, then burst out laughing.

"Ha ha! What a story!"

"Monkey no talk? He serious?"

"Stupid human!"

It feels weird to have a room full of monkeys making fun of you, and you aren't quite sure how to deal with it.

"All right, enough! Don't be rude to our guest!" First Mate Manfred shouts at the class. Once the monkeys calm down, Manfred turns to you and indicates to one of the chairs. "Have a seat."

The stink is much worse as you get close to the other monkeys, so you cover your face with your shirt as you shuffle over to a chair.

The monkeys do not look impressed with your obvious discomfort.

"Aye, we smell. Get use to it!" one of the monkeys with a blue starred bandana shouts.

You lower your eyes so as not to offend them further.

"Don't forget the Code, Monkey Moby. Scurvy Spat here is a guest of Captain Yogger."

"Yeah, yeah," the one called Monkey Moby growls, "I just hungry."

"I'm sure Norman Nopants will have something good for us to eat soon enough," the First Mate affirms.

"More like Nausea Norman," Monkey Moby groans. Apparently that's a joke, because all the other monkeys cackle with laughter.

"I'm really sorry," you uncover your nose and try your best to sound friendly, "this is just all so new and strange to me . . . I'm a little confused."

As soon as you finish speaking, the smallest monkey of the group jumps up on the table and struts over to you. He can't be more than a foot tall, but is dressed in a miniature version of the captain's outfit.

"I's Mini Mate, 'nd I's gunna make it real clear. If ye wan' t' be part o' th' crew," he hisses at you, "ye gots' t' be attenin' class an' bein' real nice, like, ye understand?!"

The monkey may be small, but he's got a scary look in his eye. You make a mental note to be extra careful around this one.

"I understand," you reply meekly.

A few of the other monkeys laugh at you, for some reason, but not Mini Mate; he frowns and crosses his arms.

"Cap't named ye well. Ye are a real Scurvy Spat!" he grunts as he leaps off the table and back to his seat.

"I'm sorry for the confusion, I'm not trying to be rude . . . I tried to tell the captain earlier – I don't know how I got here. I just want to go home."

The First Mate tilts his head slightly to the side and observes you with curious eyes.

"Then it appears you've joined us at just the right time. We're about to begin a lesson in the Grammar of Story. It seems like a little mindstorming might be good for you."

EXERCISE #1: MINDSTORMING

Okay, everyone quiet down. Welcome to class, Scurvy Spat. In case you didn't notice, we're a band of monkey-pirates who love to study all kinds of stories. Captain Yogger believes story is mighty important, no matter what types of stories you want to tell. By learning the Grammar of Story, you'll be able to sail with ease across the sea of any story.

So, get your mind ready to storm! We will be doing a lot of exercises in this class. Since this is Scurvy Spat's first day, we'll start with some practice exercises. Now Spat, don't worry about doing things "right" or "wrong" in this room. Just come up with lots of ideas. It shouldn't take long; there's no reason to overthink it. Put on your pirate hat, be creative and have fun!

But first, in order for you to do some mindstorming, I had to mindstorm my own list of categories. Take a look at these and circle the ones that you like.

1.	Places you'd love to visit	11.	Awful ice cream flavors
2.	Your favorite books	12.	Board games
3.	Movies that make you sad	13.	Types of candy
4.	Best/worst birthday presents	14.	Animated characters
5.	Colors	15.	Things at an amusement park
6.	Things monkeys throw	16.	Household chores
7.	Jelly bean flavors	17.	Things that belong in a kitchen
8.	Things to take on vacation	18.	Types of sports
9.	Pieces of furniture	19.	Tasty fruits
10.	People you know	20.	Animals you'd like as a pet

Let's take number 5: Colors. Mindstorm your own list of colors. I'll do the first few for you:

1. Orange
2. Blue
3. Cyan

4. Magenta
5. Chartreuse
6. _black_

7. _turquoise_
8. _beige_
9. _yellow_

That wasn't so hard, was it?

Now, choose one of my mindstormed categories that you liked and circled and come up with 8 things for it, just like we did for color.

Category: _Things monkies throw_

1. _banana_
2. _pillow_
3. _poop_
4. _branches_

5. _leaves_
6. _ice_
7. _oranges_
8. _pencils_

12

Pick something else from the list and do it again:

Category: _____

1. _____ 5. _____

2. _____ 6. _____

3. _____ 7. _____

4. _____ 8. _____

Now let's do it for some different categories:

Make a list of 8 funny sounding words:

1. _____ 5. _____

2. _____ 6. _____

3. _____ 7. _____

4. _____ 8. _____

Make a list of 8 animals you'd love to have a conversation with:

1. _____cat_____ 5. _____snakes_____

2. _____zonkey_____ 6. _____dolphin_____

3. _____squirrel_____ 7. _____orangatan_____

4. _____tiger_____ 8. _____red panda_____

_____shark_____

Getting sick of mindstorming yet? Don't worry, we're done (for now). Although it's hard work, mindstorming is an important part of getting those creative juices flowing that will help you tell stories. It is a lot like swabbing the deck – something else you better get used to doing if you're going to be part of the Captain's crew. Swabbing the deck isn't like brushing your teeth. You don't need to be extra careful and delicate. Just keep scrubbing away until you get the job done.

RAISE THE ANCHOR AND SET SAIL

At the end of some exercises it will be time to raise the anchor and set sail.

This means it's time for you to write a story of your own!

Let me repeat, this is the time for <u>you</u> to write a story <u>on your own</u>. I won't be holding your hand; you will need to be raising up your anchor in order to let your ship move about on the water. Most monkeys and humans find this to be terrifying. So, don't worry if writing a story all on your own makes you want to run up on deck and jump overboard. Most pirate captains (maybe all of them) feel this way from time to time. I know Captain Yogger does.

After you raise the anchor and set sail, you'll be the captain of your own ship. These are your stories, write them however you like. When you're sailing out on the open ocean like you are, you can go in any direction you want. There isn't a right and wrong way. So, be free and set sail in whatever direction you feel like going.

Write the first thing that comes into your mind. And, this is the most important thing of all, DON'T WORRY IF IT'S GOOD OR BAD. Whoever thought sticking "good" and "bad" stickers on stories ought to be eaten by a kraken. Just write down whatever comes out of you without any concern over what anyone will think about it.

The work you did in the previous exercises will be your guide.

The first thing I want you to do before you start writing is to go back and read the work you did in the exercises you just completed. Does anything stand out to you? Is something interesting? What are the things you like? Then, let your story grow out of these things. If, after you get started, you get stuck or lost, you can take another look at the work you did in the exercise. Sometimes you'll find something there that will help.

As this is the first "RAISE THE ANCHOR AND SET SAIL" section, I'll walk through the process myself. First, I will go back and review the exercise to see if there's a story to tell.

In this exercise, I did a mindstorm about "things monkeys throw." I said: bananas, bean bags, water balloons, bagels, barbeques, Bunsen burners, bowling balls and broccoli.

Then I asked myself the question, "I wonder who they are throwing these things at?" The first thing that came into my mind was, "Other monkeys in a parade." I thought of a character, Monkey Mary. Then I wondered what she wanted. The first thing I thought of was, "to throw a banana at a clown." And with that I began writing:

"Once upon a time, Monkey Mary sat with her mother on the side of the street waiting for the annual Fifth of September Monkey Mountain parade. She stood next to a huge pile of bananas; she couldn't wait to throw them. This year, she really wanted to hit a clown. There were a lot of clowns in the parade, but they were always moving fast and therefore hard to hit.

When the parade began, all the monkeys that lined the street went bonkers. One old man across the way rolled a shiny red bowling ball into the marching band. When it knocked down a tuba player and a saxophonist, he jumped up and down in delight.

Monkey Mary threw a banana at the first clown she saw, but she missed.

Bagels and water balloons flew through the air. Monkey Mary's cousin, Monkey Marty, was throwing bean bags. He hit a clown with one of them. "Awh," Monkey Mary sighed.

The parade went on. The Baboons threw their barbeques, and the Black Howlers threw their broccoli. The Cotton-topped Tamarinds threw their Bunsen burners, and Monkey Mary kept on throwing bananas. All of them missed.

She only had one left. She picked it up, but she was scared. "What if I miss?" she asked.

"Don't worry, just huck it," her mother answered.

Monkey Mary did, and she missed.

She felt terrible and cried, "I'm a failure."

"No you're not, my daughter. You had fun throwing the bananas, right?"

"Yeah, I guess so."

"Well, then you don't need to worry."

Now, Scurvy Spat, go on and have fun writing your own story.

_____

_____

_____

_____

_____

_____

_____

_____

_____

_____

_____

_____

_____

_____

_____

_____

_____

_____

CHAPTER AYE ARGH

Your head is spinning from making all these lists, but it does seem to be helping. The last thing you remember of your world was going to sleep in your bed after hearing a bedtime story about an evil pirate captain.

"That's it," you say out loud as you stand up from the table. "This must all be a dream!"

It's the only thing that makes sense.

You immediately try to pinch yourself as hard as you can, hoping the pain will jar you back to your senses and you'll wake up, but to your surprise and disappointment, nothing happens.

"What a landlubber!" Missy Monkey points at you and cackles.

"Sorry, Spat. This isn't a dream," First Mate Manfred explains. "But, if you're wanting to take a nap with the fishes, I'm sure Captain Yogger can arrange it."

This causes the monkeys around you to laugh, clap their hands, and jump up and down.

You sigh and retake your seat.

"Not so fast, Spat," First Mate Manfred states as he steps over to the wall and picks up a mop, then turns and holds it out in front of you.

"What's this for?" you ask nervously.

"For swabbing the deck," he says.

You watch as all the other monkeys groan and get out of their chairs to grab mops of their own.

"But, we just spent all that time making lists. . ."

"Yeah. And after we swab the deck, I'll have you answer some more questions and make more lists, then swab some more. It's repetitive, but important."

You can hardly believe your ears.

"Is this mandatory?" you ask after a pause.

"It is if you want to be a storytelling pirate," First Mate Manfred says.

Seeing as you're a guest on their ship and don't have any other options, you reluctantly take the mop and follow the other monkeys out of the classroom.

"Yo ho, yo ho, a pirate life for me," you grumble under your breath.

EXERCISE #2: BEING SPECIFIC

You ready to keep going? Don't be terrified, there'll be no keelhauling on this ship, so just do your best. You're being creative here, mindstorming, and becoming a storyteller. Have fun with this!

OK. Now, make me another list.

But wait – Where? How? A list of what? How long should the list be? In order for me to communicate clearly to you, I have to be specific. _Being specific is a way of setting limits and creating a focus._

A better command would be: "In the space below, write a list of 12 different places you could find on a ship to take a secret nap without anyone knowing."

Do you see how being specific communicates an idea more clearly?

One easy way to be specific is to be descriptive. A simple word like "monkey" can be made more specific by adding an adjective to describe it: "yellow monkey."

Think of an animal and write it down here: _____ Cat _____

Now, circle at least three words on the following list that you can use to describe that animal.

Angry   (Skinny)   (Fuzzy)   Scary
Sad   Fat   Scaly   Bright
Happy   Squishy   Feathered   Dark
Old   (Fast)   (Beautiful)
Young   Slow   Ugly

Using the animal you created and the words you've picked from the list, describe that animal in a more specific sentence:

_____ My beautiful kitty Jay is fast and fuzzy _____

That's a much more specific animal! By describing it like this, you helped me see it very clearly in my mind. Good work!

Now add 3 adjectives to make each of these words more specific:

1.   Monkey: Stinky / Little / Yellow
2.   Jelly bean: Sugary / yummy / squishy
3.   Pirate ship: wooden / old / fast
4.   Kitten: fluffy / tiny / cute
5.   Penguin: slow / pleasant / slippery juicy
6.   Town: _____ / _____ / _____

18

Another way to be more specific is to add details about location. Make each word more specific by adding a location:

1. Monkey: On the captain's shoulder
2. Jelly bean: _____
3. Pirate ship: _In the middle of the ocean_
4. Kitten: _On the lego world_
5. Penguin _____
6. Town: _____

Another way to be more specific is to add details about activity. Make each word more specific by adding an activity.

1. Monkey: Dancing
2. Jelly bean: _____
3. Pirate ship: _Sinking_
4. Kitten: _attacking_
5. Penguin _____
6. Town: _____

Now that you've given these things 3 adjectives, a location, and an activity, can you combine them all together in one sentence? Will it make sense?

1. Monkey: The little, stinky, yellow monkey on the captain's shoulder was dancing.
2. Jelly bean: _____

3. Pirate ship: _The wooden, old_

4. Kitten: _My beautiful, fast and fuzzy kitten on the lego world is attacking_

5. Penguin _My slow, pregnant, furry penguin on an airplace is_

6. Town: _____

Combining these various details results in something really specific.

These details might come to you all at once, or you might add them in, one at a time, like this:

- Pirate
- Evil Pirate
- Evil Pirate Captain
- Evil Pirate Captain named Long John Silver
- Evil Pirate Captain named Long John Silver, who sails the high seas
- Evil Pirate Captain named Long John Silver, who has a peg leg, and who sails the high seas
- Evil Pirate Captain named Long John Silver, who has a peg leg, a parrot who speaks only gibberish, and who sails the high seas
- Evil Pirate Captain named Long John Silver, who has a peg leg, a parrot who speaks only gibberish, and who sails the high seas in search of his stolen jelly beans

That is a very specific pirate. With all those details, you aren't going to confuse the pirate I'm thinking of with another pirate with a monkey on his shoulder who steals pollywogs.

Just as First Mate Manfred finishes his sentence about the pirate who steals pollywogs, Captain Yogger Lefossa enters the room.

"Talkin' about Pollywog Perry again, are ye? That thar slugstalker be owin' me some gold!" he sneers.

Some of the other monkeys laugh and clap, but you remain silent. Captain Yogger peers at you out of the corner of his one good eye and notices you aren't smiling.

"Enjoyin' class, Scurvy Spat?"

"Yes, sir," you reply sheepishly.

"Good. I think I'll be sittin' in on th' next bit," he announces as he sits right beside you. You try to appear casual, but his hot, stinky breath sends a shiver down your spine.

"Continue, Manfred!" Captain Yogger orders as he leans his arm on your shoulder and breaths into your face.

You try your best not to cringe as Manfred clears his throat and continues with his lesson.

Now I'll help you create a very specific character. First, circle a character from this list:

Clown / Frog / Football player / Doctor / Pirate / Dolphin / Rabbit

How old is this character? 10 yrs / 15 / refuse

Where do they live? enchanted forest / / marine rescue center

What's something they like to do? jump high / swim / swift cute

What language do they speak? english / gibberish / playful

List three descriptive words (adjectives) for them: fat slimy green / speed

What do they smell like? garbage / fishy

Here is another example. Let's start with a simple thing and make it more specific. In honor of our mighty captain, I'm going to choose a jelly bean. There are millions of jelly beans in the world; how are you going to know which one I'm talking about?

- Jelly bean
- Magic jelly bean
- A magic jelly bean from the Grove of Eternal Jelly Beans
- A magic red jelly bean from the Grove of Eternal Jelly Beans
- A magic red, pomegranate-flavored jelly bean from the Grove of Eternal Jelly Beans
- A magic red, pomegranate-flavored jelly bean from the Grove of Eternal Jelly Beans that is ripe and ready for picking

"Yar! That be one delicious type o' jelly bean! Shiver me timbers! Now ye got me all excited fer me treasure," Captain Yogger raises his arms in the air and cheers.

All the other monkeys appear to cheer as well, and so you raise your arms and let out a weak sounding, "Yippie. . .!" even though you have no idea why everyone is cheering.

As you can see, a writer can use focus and choose details that will provide specific characterizations to just about anything.

Now I'll help you create a very specific object. Choose and circle one of the following:

Chair / Basketball / Car / Sweater / Ship / (Cake) / Doll / Game / Sword / Brush / Treasure chest

What color(s) is it? _____ Brown _____

List three descriptive words (adjectives) for it: ___ Chocolate, Sugary, delicious

Who owns it? _____ MY Ava's _____

What is it used for? _____ eating _____

Who considers it valuable? _____ Ava _____

Why? _____ delicious _____

Here we will do the same thing with a location. Choose and circle one of the following:

Park / City / Beach / Mountain / Lake / House / Movie theater / Island / Pirate ship

What is its name? _____

Who is there? _____

Who owns it? _____

What do people normally do here? _____

Someone is doing something here that isn't normal. What is their name? _____

What are they doing? _____

Now do it with an event. Choose and circle one of the following:

Your birthday / (Visiting grandparents) / Last class / Summer vacation / Doctor's visit / Parade

List the people who are there: _____ *Grandma   Grandpa   Ava* _____

What is one person doing? _____ *Grandma is complaining* _____ *at his ipad*

What is another person doing? _____ *Grandpa is figuring at his ipad* _____

Who wants to be there? _____ *No one* _____

Who does not want to be there? _____ *Everyone* _____

Why? _____ *They are annoying* _____

There is another way to become specific that is simple but not so easy to do: choosing the right word. It's easy to choose a quick and boring word; you could write "The lion ate food," but lions don't just "eat," they "devour" their prey. That word gives the reader a better picture of a lion in action.

Take the underlined word and write 2 or 3 words that are better suited to really show us what is happening. I'll do the first two for you:

1. Captain Yogger <u>walked</u> over to the door. *Hobbled / Waddled / Strolled*

2. Monkey Maxine <u>ate</u> some food. *Gobbled / Devoured*

3. The monkey <u>went</u> up the mast. _____ *climbed* _____

4. The deck of the ship was covered with <u>stuff</u>. _____

5. The treasure chest was <u>filled with things</u>. _____

6. The jelly bean tasted <u>good</u>. _____

7. The First Mate <u>said</u>, "Ahoy!" _____

"Good class, but let's not be forgettin' about me jelly beans! Focus be key for pirate life!" Captain Yogger leaps to his feet and stands in front of the class. He reaches into his back pocket and pulls out a map and holds it up for everyone to see. "See this here X? This be the spot where we be findin' th' Grove of Eternal Jelly Beans. Truest treasure thar be! 'Member, that thar be th' specific thing we be focusin' on fer this quest! Think about it; magic jelly beans growin' on bushes as far as th' eye can see! Ye never tasted anythin' like it before."

Every monkey in the room breaks out cheering at the description – all except for Monkey Moby, who sits with his arms crossed.

For the first time since being on board, you feel a certain bond with the monkeys; jelly beans are one of your favorite snacks and the thought of a magic jelly bean has your mouth watering, too.

"Are they really magic?" you ask one of the monkeys next to you.

But before the monkey can respond, Captain Yogger quickly folds up the map and steps right in front of your desk.

"Aye, thay be magic. The best and most powerful kind! Ya see, thay taste like tiny fruit, but are shaped like a bean, an' make me bad breath get better." As if on cue, his stinky breath wafts over to you and causes you to scrunch up your nose.

"Oh," you reply.

You're not entirely sure anymore if the jelly beans are magic after all, or if he just thinks they're magic because he's a pirate with bad breath.

"And . . . umm . . . they grow on an island? On bushes? Not, like, in a factory?" you ask nervously.

"Factory? Have ye lost yer mind, Spat! No! Thay grow on bushes, yar, row after row. Thar be a whole lot'o'beans. A whole lot. Stick around, and ye might even get a taste fer yerself."

As ridiculous as the concept of jelly beans growing on bushes is, until recently, a crew full of talking monkeys seemed equally impossible. If there really is an island full of jelly beans – magic or not – it may be well worth the trip.

CHAPTER ARGH

You lie in your new bed that night and attempt to sleep after a long day of making lists and swabbing decks. But, even though you're exhausted, you find it impossible to sleep due to the constant rocking of the ship and the sound of the four other snoring monkeys who share your room.

You try to cover your head with your pillow, but that doesn't seem to help at all, and so you lay back and stare up at the ceiling.

You can hardly believe all that's happened today. Somehow, you wound up in a world with pirates, talking monkeys, and magic jelly beans.

As you ponder these things, you gradually become aware of the sound of one of the monkeys stirring in his bed. You wonder if he's having trouble sleeping too, and consider trying to talk to him, when all of a sudden, he flies out of bed and sneaks out of the room.

"That's strange," you think to yourself.

Feeling curious about where a monkey on a pirate ship might be sneaking off to in the middle of the night, you decide to get out of bed and see where he's going.

You follow the monkey all the way to the upper deck and step outside. It's a clear night, and the moon is bigger and brighter than you've ever seen before. You stare up at it and lose yourself in the beauty, almost forgetting why you came out here in the first place.

When you finally pull your eyes away from it, you realize the monkey you were following is now standing on the railing of the ship.

The light of the moon illuminates his clothing, and you recognize the pattern of his blue bandana.

"Hey! Monkey Moby?" you call to him. "What are you doing out here?"

The monkey hisses and pulls out a little sword.

"Leave me alone!" he cries. "I leaving, and that that."

You raise your eyebrows.

"What? Why? Don't you like it here?"

"No! Why would I? Work, work, work. Make lists, swab deck. Answer question, swab deck. All we do is work!"

"But aren't you excited to go find the treasure? Doesn't that make the work worthwhile?"

Monkey Moby stomps his foot in irritation.

"You kiddin' me? No! I no want jelly beans, I want banana! You know how long it been since I had banana!?"

You shake your head; you have no idea.

"LeFossa no let us eat them," Monkey Moby cried, "say we need to focus on his treasure. Nope! Not for me. I want no work and all bananas. Bye!"

You try to call out for him to stop, but it's too late. Right in front of you, Monkey Moby leaps off the railing and into the sea.

As soon as he hits the water, a small whirlpool forms and sucks him straight into it.

"NO!" you cry, turn to run and get help, and collide right into the captain.

"Nar! Let him go," Captain Yogger says, "he made his choice."

You're afraid of the answer, but you have to ask.

"But . . . isn't he going to die?"

"Nar, nar," Captain Yogger shakes his head, "the whirlpool be magic, an' be takin' him back t' his home."

That gives you some relief, but you still can't help but feel sad about the whole thing.

"Story be mighty important," Captain Yogger continues, "far more dangerous than them sissy subjects like numbers 'n biologies'. Schoolin' gots t' be preparin' ye for fightn' kraken!"

You nod in agreement even though you don't really understand what a kraken is, or why you'd ever be fighting one. You want to ask Captain Yogger if it's true that he doesn't feed the monkeys bananas, but you're afraid if you do, he might get angry, so instead you remain silent and watch as he pops a yellow jelly bean into his mouth and resumes talking:

"Monkey Moby not be the first t' go, ya see. Ev'ry monkey be followin' what he feel th' most significant story. If helpin' on me adventure ain't what me monkey mates be wantin', thay be free to leave at any time an' seek thar own."

Captain Yogger's words haunt you as you return to your bed that night. You wonder if you could leave and go home the same way. It would be scary to jump off a moving ship into the ocean. But, if he's telling the truth, that magic will take you home, maybe you should jump too?

EXERCISE #3: SETTING

In order to have a story, you must first have a world. Setting is what we call the location where a group of characters live and act and where the stories about them take place.

Some stories begin with the setting; their opening sentence might be something like this:

Long ago, in a galaxy far away . . .   Inside the attic at ol' Uncle Frank's . . .
Once upon a time, in Sherwood Forest . . .   In the Valley of the Giants . . .
On a dark and stormy night . . .   Thousands of miles under the Earth . . .

Other stories take time to reveal their time and place. It might take you a few pages to find out the setting of the story takes place in the days of the Wild West, or maybe in another country.

Setting tells us the time and place where this story takes place. Establishing time and place is one way to give your story world some boundaries.

Write the name of one of your favorite stories: ___Harry Potter___

What are some places in this story? ___Hogwarts London Diagon Alley___

In what time did this story take place? ___Modern times___

Write the name of one of another of your favorite stories: _____

What are some places in this story? _____

In what time did this story take place? _____

PLACE

List 5 places you go every day:

1. ___Dance___
2. ___Home___
3. ___Car___
4. ___Biltmore Bar___
5. ___Bathroom___

List 4 places where there is water:

1. ___Biltmore Lake___
2. ___Waterfall___
3. ___Cup of water___
4. ___sea cave___

List 2 places where there is no water:

1. ___Dessert___
2. _____

List 4 places you would rather be now:

1. ___Disney___
2. ___Paris___
3. ___Hawaii___
4. ___Dance___

List 3 places you feel safe:

1. ___Home___
2. ___Bed___
3. ___Dance___

List 4 places you would like to explore:

1. ___Giant Candy Gingerbread___
2. _____
3. _____
4. _____

As a story creator, the more specific you can be about the place you are describing, the more your reader will be able to understand what you mean.

On the left is a list of descriptions, and on the right are some places. Connect a description with a place by either drawing a line to it or writing the letter of the place next to the description:

_____ Grandma's. . .	a. School
_____ The old. . .	b. Car
_____ The broken. . .	c. Beach
_____ The burning. . .	d. Bridge
_____ A closed. . .	e. Art studio
_____ The enormous. . .	f. Playground
_____ A beautiful. . .	g. Church
_____ The fun. . .	h. Hamburger restaurant
_____ The candy. . .	i. Mall
_____ A scary. . .	j. Attic

Here is a list of descriptive words you can use to describe a place in more detail:

Cold	Electric	Yellow	Made of wood
Frozen	Golden	Pink	On fire
Dirty	Sparkling	Purple	Painted
Covered in mud	Sharp	Incredibly massive	Sticky
Filled with bugs	Stinky	Unbelievably small	Full of snails
Broken	Red	Brand new	Bouncy
Made of chocolate	Blue	Slippery	Twinkling

Select a few of the items from the list to help you write a sentence that describes a place. Example:

1. Place: Beach
Selected items: Warm and Sticky / Brown / Full of snails
Sentence: The brown beach was warm, sticky, and full of snails!

2. Place: _____

Selected items: _____

Sentence: _____

3. Place: _____

Selected items: _____

Sentence: _____

4. Place: _____

Selected items: _____

Sentence: _____

Now, try to describe a place in even greater detail. Here is an example:

Place: Chocolate factory
1. *Cold, so that the chocolate doesn't melt*
2. *Huge bars of chocolate everywhere*
3. *Cavernous rooms*
4. *The walls are all painted different shades of brown*
5. *Boxes are stacked everywhere*

1. Choose one of your examples of place. Describe this place in greater detail.

Place: _____

1. _____
2. _____
3. _____
4. _____
5. _____

2. Choose one of your examples of place. Describe this place in greater detail.

Place: _____

1. _____
2. _____
3. _____
4. _____
5. _____

3. Choose one of your examples of place. Describe this place in greater detail.

Place: _____

1. _____
2. _____
3. _____
4. _____
5. _____

You can also use your five senses to help you describe a place.

Choose a place: _____

What do you see? _____

Does it smell like anything? What? _____

What kinds of sounds can be heard there? _____

What is something there you can touch? _____

What does that object feel like? _____

Try to find something there you can taste. What is it? _____

Can you describe its taste? _____

Now that you have some ideas, go through the following places and make them more specific:

1. House: A haunted mansion.

2. Beach: A rocky shore with seashells all around.

3. Ship: A broken, old, sinking ship.

4. Store: _____

5. Road: _____

6. Desk: _____

7. Farm: _____

8. City: _____

9. Office: _____

10. School: _____

11. Mall: _____

12. Factory: _____

13. Village: _____

14. Island: _____

15. Country: _____

16. Planet: _____

TIME

Another way storytellers can focus a specific setting is time. Examples of time are: 5 o'clock, the 1950s, summertime, time to go, bedtime, a long time ago, her wedding day, showtime. . .

List 10 different specific times a story could take place. Use real times, imaginary ones, or ones from your favorite stories.

1. _____   6. _____

2. _____   7. _____

3. _____   8. _____

4. _____   9. _____

5. _____   10. _____

Like with places, time is made stronger by giving it more specific details.

Choose one of the times you wrote down. Then add 5 details, adjectives, or descriptions to it.

Time: The day before Christmas   Time: _____

1. Inside the tent   1. _____

2. During the winter   2. _____

3. After the big storm   3. _____

4. _____   4. _____

5. _____   5. _____

Time: _____   Time: _____

1. _____   1. _____

2. _____   2. _____

3. _____   3. _____

4. _____   4. _____

5. _____   5. _____

EVENT

Another detail a writer can use to create a story world is an event. Events combine place and time in a specific moment or activity. Draw a line under the "event" in the following sentences:

1. Later that day, we walked over to the yard sale.
2. After school, I had a big graduation ceremony.
3. My favorite time of year is grandpa's birthday.
4. Skating parties are the best at my uncle's ice rink.
5. I went to the summer fair the other day.
6. Every kid who wants to see space must attend space camp.
7. This year, I sang and danced at the Camp Wannemakeit talent show.
8. My dad still talks about the first time he went to a Monkeys' concert.
9. On July 20, 1969, people gathered around televisions to watch man walk on the moon!
10. The Annual Banana Picnic is every monkey's dream.

On the left is a list of times, and on the right are some places and events. Draw a line or write the letter to connect a time to the places and events in order to create a basic setting:

_____ After. . .	a. New Year's Day
_____ During. . .	b. The birthday party
_____ Before. . .	c. Recess
_____ Earlier than. . .	d. School
_____ Right at. . .	e. The magic show
_____ Tomorrow is. . .	f. The movie ended
_____ Many years after. . .	g. My favorite holiday
_____ The night before. . .	h. The hurricane
_____ The morning of. . .	i. The doctor's appointment
_____ At 3:15 p.m., Tuesday. . .	j. The Light Festival
_____ At the crack of dawn. . .	h. Wednesday night dance party

Mindstorm a list of several different events. The more specific, the better.

1. Scurvy Spat's first day on the ship.
2. The day the fire station burned down.
3. _____
4. _____
5. _____
6. _____
7. _____
8. _____
9. _____
10. _____
11. _____
12. _____

31

Take 5 of your events, and make them very specific in terms of time and place:

Example 1: The Monkeys celebrated their annual Banana Picnic on Tuesday at the top of the volcano.

Example 2: The Camp Wannemakeit talent show is in the community room tonight at ten o'clock.

1. _____

2. _____

3. _____

4. _____

5. _____

This time, instead of describing one event in greater detail, choose 5 events from your events list and describe the weather during each one.

Example: The morning of the banana bread festival was sunny and hot.

1. _____

2. _____

3. _____

4. _____

5_____

Though a story creator certainly doesn't have to start with setting, it's a simple way to begin building a foundation for your story world. Establishing the time, place, and some of the events that happen in your story will help give you focus when creating all the special things that will be in that world.

CHAPTER ARGH AYE

"Rise n' shine, Scurvy Spat!" Monkey Martin growls at you as he pulls off your blanket.

"What time is it?" you mumble as you wipe the sleep from your eyes.

"What kind o' dumb question is that?" Monkey Martin sneers. "I don't know how they do things in Northern Canmerico, but here, sun up mean all up!"

Despite being completely exhausted, you stumble out of bed and do your best to look alert as you follow your monkey roommate down the hall and onto the main deck. You've only been here a full day, but you're getting the sense that Captain Yogger runs a very tight ship.

As soon as you step out into the blinding light of morning, you realize all the monkeys are lined up on deck and are facing the captain.

"Yar! Ye bein' late again, Monkey Martin. Not a good sign o' dedication, if ye be askin' me," Captain Yogger frowns as the two of you join the other monkeys.

"Apologizes, Cap'n. T'was the human's fault," Monkey Martin announces innocently.

"What?" you exclaim. "Was not!"

"Was too!" he sneers back at you.

"Enough!" Captain Yogger snaps. "Thar be no fightin' amongst th' crew on me ship, ye hear?"

Although you feel quite upset at how Monkey Martin was blaming you for making them late, you decide it's best not to argue.

"Yes sir," you reply meekly.

Captain Yogger winks with his one good eye, turns his back to you, and – much to your surprise – pulls out a gun.

You don't have time to be afraid, though, because he immediately points it into the sky and pulls the trigger.

BANG!

The next thing you know, all the monkeys drop face first on the ground and start doing vigorous push-ups.

"Ahem," Captain Yogger clears his throat when he notices that you're just standing there, watching.

"Oh. Me too?" you squeak.

"It be how we start th' mornin', Spat. Pirate life wit' me be more than just treasurin' and learnin' about story! If ye want t' stay here, ye best be joinin' in."

You nod with as much enthusiasm as you can muster and lower yourself to the deck; it seems that Captain Yogger's expectations for a morning routine are very different than anything you've ever experienced at home.

Of course, it doesn't end with push-ups. For the next thirty minutes, Captain Yogger has you and all the monkeys running laps around the ship, climbing ropes, and doing various stretches.

"A fit crew be a mighty crew!" he laughs as you jog by.

After what feels like ages, he shoots his gun into the air again and everyone stops. You breathe a sigh of relief, but it's short lived. The morning doesn't end with exercise.

"Time for chores!"

EXERCISE #4: VALUES

Now that you understand what setting is, we'll look at values.

Values are things that are valuable. Things can be valuable because:

- They are important (your teddy bear, the Declaration of Independence).
- They are expensive (ocean front real estate, gold plated teeth).
- They are useful (electricity, a pirate's sword).
- They are good for you (cod liver oil, high moral rectitude).
- They give pleasure (chocolate, monkey hugs).

Values reflect what is believed to be important, worthwhile or useful, and are critical in story. Stories are born out of values; they lurk behind almost everything in the story world.

List some objects, places, or people that are valuable to you in your life.

1. My best friend Captain Yogger
2. Banana pudding on dry toast
3. Sunshine after a storm
4. _____
5. _____
6. _____
7. _____
8. _____
9. _____
10. _____

11. _____
12. _____
13. _____
14. _____
15. _____
16. _____
17. _____
18. _____
19. _____
20. _____

CULTURAL VALUES

Certain cultures choose to put a higher emphasis – or value – on certain things. Mindstorm some things you think your culture values. Be as specific as possible.

Example: A national monument / Public transportation / Coconut football

1. _____
2. _____
3. _____

4. _____
5. _____
6. _____

What are some things you think that your home country does *not* value?

Example: Smoking / Throwing banana peels at strangers / Hockey

1. _____   4. _____

2. _____   5. _____

3. _____   6. _____

This is an example of values based on *cultural opinion*. These six things have or don't have value because the culture says so. Someone from a different country might value different things, just like us monkey pirates have values that might differ from yours.

USEFULNESS

Some cultures put a higher value on some objects because of their usefulness in doing the things which that culture values. For example, in a culture that values violence, powerful weapons will be objects that are considered valuable, but in a peace-loving culture, people may despise weapons and value forgiveness and reconciliation instead.

On the left are some types of cultures, and on the right are some things those cultures might value. Connect the culture to the thing it would value most.

_____ Scientific culture	a. Text books
_____ Fearful culture	b. Swords
_____ Hard-working culture	c. Big walls
_____ Violent culture	d. Candy factories
_____ School culture	e. Instruments
_____ Sugar-loving culture	f. Tools

List 5 things that are useful for a certain type of culture.

A culture that values jelly beans: A culture that values board games:

1. _____   1. _____

2. _____   2. _____

3. _____   3. _____

4. _____   4. _____

5. _____   5. _____

A culture that values high quality food:

1. _____
2. _____
3. _____
4. _____
5. _____

A culture that values coconut football:

1. _____
2. _____
3. _____
4. _____
5. _____

A culture that values furry animals:

1. _____
2. _____
3. _____
4. _____
5. _____

A culture that values entertainment:

1. _____
2. _____
3. _____
4. _____
5. _____

Create your own values and give some things that would be useful for that value.

A culture that values: _____

1. _____
2. _____
3. _____
4. _____
5. _____

A culture that values: _____

1. _____
2. _____
3. _____
4. _____
5. _____

A culture that values: _____

1. _____
2. _____
3. _____
4. _____
5. _____

A culture that values: _____

1. _____
2. _____
3. _____
4. _____
5. _____

A culture that values: _____

1. _____
2. _____
3. _____
4. _____
5. _____

A culture that values: _____

1. _____
2. _____
3. _____
4. _____
5. _____

NON-PHYSICAL VALUES

Things that are valuable are not always something you can touch. For example, some people value love, music, justice, generosity, a beautiful sunset, or a TV show.

List 10 values that are non-material objects:

1. _____   6. _____
2. _____   7. _____
3. _____   8. _____
4. _____   9. _____
5. _____   10. _____

There are also non-physical values people hold in common. Often these are things that are necessary for a group to work together, such as peace, justice, family, education, or health.

Make a list of some things that you think Captain Yogger and us monkeys might value.

1. Dancing   9. _____
2. Searching for treasure   10. _____
3. Rescuing monkey slaves   11. _____
4. _____   12. _____
5. _____   13. _____
6. _____   14. _____
7. _____   15. _____
8. _____   16. _____

Often, people who have a non-physical value will care a lot about certain physical objects or places that help them appreciate the non-physical things they value. For example, we value searching for treasure (a non-physical value), so we've got a treasure map, compass, magic telescope, and ship to help us. We also like to travel to remote islands in order to look for treasure on them.

What are some examples of physical objects and/or places that people who have certain non-physical values might care about?

Non-physical value: Knowledge of space   Non-physical value: Dancing

1. Telescopes   1. _____
2. Observatories   2. _____
3. Rocket ships   3. _____

Non-physical value: Storytelling

1. _____

2. _____

3. _____

Non-physical value: Rescuing slaves

1. _____

2. _____

3. _____

Non-physical value: _____

1. _____

2. _____

3. _____

Non-physical value: _____

1. _____

2. _____

3. _____

Non-physical value: _____

1. _____

2. _____

3. _____

Non-physical value: _____

1. _____

2. _____

3. _____

MORAL VALUES

Cultures also hold another sort of values that are called moral values. These values are things a group or community believes to be right and good. They can be things like honesty, generosity, patience, cooperativeness, or kindness.

List 10 moral values:

1. _____

2. _____

3. _____

4. _____

5. _____

6. _____

7. _____

8. _____

9. _____

10. _____

Go back and circle the items on that list that you think Captain Yogger and us monkey mates would also value.

A culture's moral values often lead that culture to create laws, rules, and customs that reinforce that value. Take the following moral values and write three laws, rules, or customs that support it.

Moral Value: Peacefulness

1. Quiet hours are between 10 p.m. and 7 a.m.

2. No fighting while on school property.

3. Negotiate for peace before taking military action.

38

Moral value: Freedom of Speech

1. _____

2. _____

3. _____

Moral value: Hard work pays off

1. _____

2. _____

3. _____

Moral value: Honoring elders

1. _____

2. _____

3. _____

Moral value: Love your enemies

1. _____

2. _____

3. _____

Now create your own moral value. It could be one of the ones on your list of ten values, or it could be a new one.

Moral value: _____

1. _____

2. _____

3. _____

Moral value: _____

1. _____

2. _____

3. _____

Moral value: _____

1. _____

2. _____

3. _____

Moral value: _____

1. _____

2. _____

3. _____

NEGATIVE VALUES

People and cultures can also value things that aren't normally considered good. They can be things like lying, cheating, stealing, shouting, demanding your way, or even violence. These are negative things but people can still value them.

Negative value: Making monkeys slaves
1. Chains

2. _____

3. _____

Negative value: Swearing

1. _____

2. _____

3. _____

Negative value: Hoarding wealth

1. _____

2. _____

3. _____

Negative value: _____

1. _____

2. _____

3. _____

BONUS QUESTION: When someone has a negative value, they can't always be open and truthful about it. Negative values tend to be hidden or acted out in ways that prevent the person from being punished. What are some ways a character in a story can hide the fact that they have a negative value, or avoid punishment for it?

Choose one of the negative values above: _____

How could they hide this value or avoid punishment for it?_____

_____

_____

"HEAVE HO!"

Think you got the hang of it? Whenever I yell "HEAVE HO!" be prepared to do some more difficult exercises. These are designed to challenge you, so don't get discouraged if they are too difficult.

Okay, let's start. When a society or culture values something, you will find evidence of that value everywhere. The society that values "law and order" will create and support things devoted to it, like laws, court rooms, police officers, and prisons. The society that values "education" will have things like school curriculum, school buildings, and teachers.

Write down a cultural value we pirates have and give "evidence" of that value on our ship. (Use one of the example values from above if you need ideas.)

Value: Exercise

1. Workout routines
2. Climbing up and down the mast
3. Swabbing the deck
4. Swinging from the lines of the ship
5. Dancing

Value: _____

1. _____
2. _____
3. _____
4. _____
5. _____

Value: _____

1. _____
2. _____
3. _____
4. _____
5. _____

SCRATCH YER NOGGIN'

While the "HEAVE HO!" section is to challenge you, the SCRATCH YER NOGGIN' section is to test your memory on past sections.

Define:

1. Setting: _____

2. Place: _____

3. Time: _____

4. Events: _____

5. What are values? _____

6. Being specific is a way of _____ and _____

7. Add 3 adjectives to make each of these words more specific:

Rat: _____ / _____ / _____

Lion: _____ / _____ / _____

Tree house: _____ / _____ / _____

Swimming pool: _____ / _____ / _____

School house: _____ / _____ / _____

8. Give an example of place and add 3 adjectives to make it more specific.

_____: _____ / _____ / _____

_____: _____ / _____ / _____

_____: _____ / _____ / _____

9. Give an example of time and add 3 adjectives to make it more specific.

_____: _____ / _____ / _____

_____: _____ / _____ / _____

_____: _____ / _____ / _____

10. What is the value of having a specific setting? _____

_____

_____

EXERCISE #5: SIGNIFICANCE

To be significant is to be worthy of attention. As an author builds a story world, there may be ordinary things that become significant and have special importance in the story.

Mindstorm a list of 20 simple objects you might find in a story. I'll start a few for you:

1. A watch
2. Desk
3. A piece of paper
4. _____
5. _____
6. _____
7. _____
8. _____
9. _____
10. _____

11. _____
12. _____
13. _____
14. _____
15. _____
16. _____
17. _____
18. _____
19. _____
20. _____

Next, be specific. If I say, "I saw a piece of paper," you won't know what paper I'm talking about, and you'll certainly assume it isn't worth much attention. But, if I give it extra details, you might find it's very significant indeed, especially if I say, "I saw Captain Yogger take out a piece of paper hidden in his jacket, but when he saw me coming, he put it away."

Take some of the objects you wrote above and make them specific by adding three details.

1. A watch: a gift / wristwatch / old
2. Desk: ornate / in president's office / rarely used
3. A piece of paper: the captain's / hidden / valuable
4. _____ : _____ / _____ / _____
5. _____ : _____ / _____ / _____
6. _____ : _____ / _____ / _____
7. _____ : _____ / _____ / _____
8. _____ : _____ / _____ / _____
9. _____ : _____ / _____ / _____
10. _____ : _____ / _____ / _____

The more detail you give to an object, the more significant you make it. So, if you don't want a dog to be significant in your story, you probably shouldn't spend too much time describing it when you could be describing something you want the reader to focus on.

But, details alone do not make an item significant. Things are significant for a reason.

Now that you have a list of simple objects with details, write a sentence that includes some reason why they are significant.

1. Watch: The old watch was given to the character by his favorite teacher.

2. Desk: The President used this ornate, rarely used desk, to sign the new law.

3. A piece of paper: Captain Yogger keeps his treasure map hidden inside his coat.

4. _____

_____

5. _____

_____

6. _____

_____

7. _____

_____

8. _____

_____

9. _____

_____

10. _____

_____

An object could be significant for all kinds of different reasons. One reason is the kind of story the object is in. Comedies are stories that make us laugh, so the object might be significant because it is funny. Dramas are often serious and make us cry, so the significant object might be something that is sentimental or emotionally valuable to a character. Horror stories are scary, so the significant object could be something creepy. In fantasy stories, anything can happen, so they often have magical significant objects. And, of course, romance stories are all about love, so they will likely have some kind of object that has emotional or romantic significance.

Take an object from your list, and change the significance it has based on the different type of story:

1. Object: *Ring*
    Romance: Wedding ring
    Fantasy: A magic ring
    Comedy: A circus ring
    Horror: A cryptic, ancient ring that glows when a ghost is nearby
    Drama: Grandmother's ring

2. Object (choose one): table, chair, sofa, carpet

Romance: _____

Fantasy: _____

Comedy: _____

Horror: _____

Drama: _____

3. Object (choose one): ship, car, truck, airplane, horse

Romance: _____

Fantasy: _____

Comedy: _____

Horror: _____

Drama: _____

4. Object (choose one): sword, walking stick, pencil, chopstick, magic wand

Romance: _____

Fantasy: _____

Comedy: _____

Horror: _____

Drama: _____

5. Object: _____

Romance: _____

Fantasy: _____

Comedy: _____

Horror: _____

Drama: _____

Think of a story you like, then pick a significant object in that story, and write why:

1. Story: <u>Star Wars</u>   Significant object: <u>Light saber</u>

Why: <u>A light saber is used to fight Darth Vader.</u>

2. Story: _____ Significant object: _____

Why: _____

3. Story: _____ Significant object: _____

Why: _____

4. Story: _____ Significant objoot: _____

Why: _____

5. Story: _____ Significant object: _____

Why: _____

6. Story: _____ Significant object: _____

Why: _____

NAMES

Another way to increase the significance of something is to give it a name. An ordinary piece of paper isn't very significant, but when it is given the name "Treasure Map" because of the special marks drawn on it, it becomes significant.

What other names could you give to a piece of paper to make it significant?

1. The Declaration of Independence

2. A report card

3. Money

4. Family picture

5. _____

6. _____

7. _____

8. _____

9. _____

10. _____

WORLDLINGS

Most story worlds are populated with worldlings. These could include animals, people, creatures, and groups. These are living things that have meaning and weight within the story world.

A worldling is not a specific character, but a group of characters/types of creatures that are significant locals in that world.

Examples:

       Talking wild animals (like in fairy tales)

       Ewoks (like in *Star Wars*)

       Living stuffed animals/toys (like in *Toy Story*)

       Angry flying monkeys (the ones from the *Wizard of Oz* gave Monkey Mo Mo nightmares)

       Wizards (like in *Harry Potter*, or *The Lord of the Rings*)

Choose 10 different stories you can think of that have interesting types of worldlings in them. What or who are they?

1. Snow White and the seven dwarves

2. _____

3. _____

4. _____

5. _____

6. _____

7. _____

8. _____

9. _____

10. _____

Create a list of different potential worldlings for a story you might create (remember, these are whatever characters populate the story world).

1. Dogs you can carry in a purse

2. Elementary school teachers

3. Aliens with rainbow-colored skin

4. Stinky monkeys

5. _____

6. _____

7. _____

8. _____

9. _____

10. _____

Choose some of your examples of worldlings. In a few sentences, describe them more specifically.

1. Worldling: Stinky monkeys

"A band of monkeys were exiled from their homeland, Monkey Mountain, because they were too stinky. They wandered aimlessly until they were discovered by Captain Yogger. He brought them onto his ship, and they have sailed with him ever since."

2. Worldling: _____

_____

_____

_____

3. Worldling: _____

_____

_____

_____

47

4. Worldling: _____

_____

_____

_____

5. Worldling: _____

_____

_____

_____

Though place is a part of the setting, some places, like objects, can have special weight and meaning in a story. Every story takes place somewhere, but in some stories, that somewhere is truly significant.

What city were you born in? _____

That city is significant to your story, because you were born there!

On the left is a list of objects, and on the right are some places. Connect the object to a place that you think would make it significant.

_____ Logs   a. The Arctic

_____ Gloves   b. A school

_____ Paintbrushes   c. A hospital

_____ Medicine   d. A fireplace

_____ Books   e. An art studio

Some significant places in stories are real, like *Tom Sawyer* taking place in the Deep South. Other significant places are imaginary, like Gotham City in Batman, Hogwarts in Harry Potter, or Never-Never Land in Peter Pan. In either case these places are specific and necessary – they are significant – the story wouldn't be the same if it were set somewhere else.

Write down a story you like: _____

Can you think of 4 significant places in that story?

1. _____   3. _____

2. _____   4. _____

Try it again with another story:

1. _____   3. _____

2. _____   4. _____

"HEAVE HO!"

Take an object you might be used to seeing in one type of story and write a line describing how it could still be significant for a different type of story. I'll do the first one so you understand what I mean:

Object: A wedding ring
    Romance: A symbol of marriage.
    Fantasy: The monster is freed from his curse if he gets married and wears a ring.
    Comedy: A husband lost his wife's wedding ring.
    Horror: A ghost haunts a wedding ring.
    Drama: A woman is forced to hide her wedding ring to survive.

1. Object: A long steel sword, or one of your own: _____

    Romance: _____

    Fantasy: _____

    Comedy: _____

    Horror: _____

    Drama: _____

2. Object: A beautiful, delicate doll, or one of your own: _____

    Romance: _____

    Fantasy: _____

    Comedy: _____

    Horror: _____

    Drama: _____

Do the same thing, but with worldlings:

1. Worldlings: Professional ballet dancers, or one of your own: _____

    Romance: _____

    Fantasy: _____

    Comedy: _____

    Horror: _____

    Drama: _____

2. Worldlings: Soldiers fighting in a war, or one of your own: _____

      Romance: _____

      Fantasy: _____

      Comedy: _____

      Horror: _____

      Drama: _____

Do the same thing, but with a place:

1. Place: Haunted mansion, or one of your own: _____

      Romance: _____

      Fantasy: _____

      Comedy: _____

      Horror: _____

      Drama: _____

2. Place: An amusement park, or one of your own: _____

      Romance: _____

      Fantasy: _____

      Comedy: _____

      Horror: _____

      Drama: _____

SCRATCH YER NOGGIN'

You've now learned some of the basic elements of story world building. You have lists of setting (place, time and events), significant objects, and worldlings. When these are all put together, you've got a solid foundation for a story world.

For each of the following sentences, identify the different world building elements.

1: Last month, when we set sail from Banana Bay, a monkey cried into a banana peel.

    Place: Banana Bay
    Time: Last month
    Event: Set sail
    Significant object: Banana peel
    Worldling: Monkey

2: Over 300 years ago, on the bottom of the sea, a baby pollywog chewed on a piece of wood.

    Place: _____

    Time: _____

    Event: _____

    Significant object: _____

    Worldling: _____

3: Last year, on the ancient Island of Elders, we stumbled upon a zombie pirate dance party. We used makeup to disguise ourselves and sneak past them.

    Place: _____

    Time: _____

    Event: _____

    Significant object: _____

    Worldling: _____

4: Late every night in the Forests of Muse, the local parrots take out their song books and sing a concert for all who will listen.

    Place: _____

    Time: _____

    Event: _____

    Significant object: _____

    Worldling: _____

Now, I want you to mix up all of these elements to create new sentences. Take one element, at random, from each category above. Then use each element to write what will be a crazy sentence.

Follow this example:

Place: Banana Bay

Time: Late at night

Event: Dance party

Significant object: Song books

Worldling: Baby Kraken

Sentence: "Late at night, at Banana Bay, there was a big dance party with a baby kraken singing from a song book."

Place: _____

Time: _____

Event: _____

Significant object: _____

Worldling: _____

Sentence: _____

_____

One more time, but with a different set of random examples.

Place: _____

Time: _____

Event: _____

Significant object: _____

Worldling: _____

Sentence: _____

_____

Place, time, events, significant objects, and worldlings are a few of the tools a writer uses to create a foundation for his story world. But, these are just the beginning. Next, we'll introduce some other elements a storyteller can use to make a story world realistic and interesting.

RAISE THE ANCHOR AND SET SAIL

Set sail and write a story of your own. Remember, you can write anything you want. Don't worry about it making any sense. Look back at the exercises you did, grab a significant object and a worldling, and just start writing.

_____

_____

_____

_____

_____

_____

_____

_____

_____

_____

_____

_____

_____

_____

_____

_____

_____

_____

_____

_____

_____

_____

_____

_____

_____

_____

_____

_____

CHAPTER ARGH AYE AYE

You've been assigned the job of scrubbing the floors. Another one of the great values Captain Yogger is trying to teach the crew, you guess.

You're working with Mini Mate, Monkey Maxine, and Monkey Monica. You haven't had much interaction with Monkey Maxine or Monkey Monica yet, but you've heard them lots in class.

Monkey Maxine is way too eager in her desire to please the First Mate. She also doesn't seem to have very helpful answers – everything she says is kind of obvious. You get the sense that she doesn't really care about the class, almost as if she were just happy to be doing something amusing and easy.

Monkey Monica is similar. Only, instead of trying to please the First Mate, she always cracks jokes and plays dumb. Even now, she acts like she doesn't care much and isn't really doing much to help clean the floor.

Suddenly, you realize you're now thinking about monkeys like you would people.

"If I'm really in a different world," you think to yourself, "then I guess these monkeys are all Worldlings."

This has been two of the strangest days of your life.

"Arg! Werk harder!" Mini Mate shouts at you as soon as he notices your mind has been wandering.

"Sorry." You try to get back at it, but scrubbing floors really doesn't interest you. "Why do all you monkeys stay here? I mean, you're not even allowed to eat bananas, right?"

Mini Mate growls at you, but it's Monkey Maxine who responds:

"Ehhh. We here to help Captain Yogger," she shrugs. "Bananas make us smell bad, anyway."

You fight the urge to tell her that they already smell bad.

"Why does the captain need help, though? He already seems to have a lot of jelly beans. Why does he need more?"

The three monkeys exchange uneasy glances.

"Well . . ." Monkey Monica starts, "Captain Yogger have kind of . . . you know . . . bad breath." She whispers the last part.

"Uh-huh," you nod, "he's a pirate."

"He think if he gets magic jelly beans, he never have bad breath again."

"Hmmm," you think that it makes sense. But, could a jelly bean – even if it was magic – really make such bad breath smell any better?

You continue working with the other three monkeys until your back aches. The worst part is you know you have at least another hour of scrubbing floors to do.

"This is boring," Monkey Monica announces to you. "I want to nap."

"Me too," Monkey Maxine agrees.

"Nar!" Mini Mate hisses. "Ye must be werking. Capt'n's orders!"

"It not big deal," Monkey Maxine insists. "I skip chore all the time. You in, Scurvy Spat?"

You hesitate. You probably should stay, but you aren't really sure what the point of scrubbing the floor is in the first place, since dirty monkeys are constantly walking across it and spilling things. Will anyone even notice if you scrub the floors or not? Plus, you didn't get a great sleep last night. A nap would be really nice right about now.

"Sure," you shrug.

Monkey Monica and Monkey Maxine clap happily and – despite the frustrated grunts of Mini Mate – the three of you leave him and sneak away.

"Will he tell on us?"

"Not if he know what good for him," Monkey Maxine growls.

"It don't matter if he do tell," Monkey Monica adds with a grin, "I's the Captain's favorite. We be fine."

You assume Monkey Monica is right and knows what she is doing, but that's proven wrong almost as soon as you leave the room where you're supposed to be working.

Standing at the other end of the hall is Captain Yogger.

"Avast. Tryin' t' sneak away, are ye?"

You can't believe it! How did he know?

"It's not what it looks like. . ."

"Hello Captain!" Monkey Monica attempts to sound charming. "We just want to go for little walk, is all!"

"Oh, I see!" Captain Yogger raises an eyebrow and twirls his thick mustache with the end of his hook. "I suppos' ye think that be fine, then? T' go around an' do as ye please while ev'ryone else be werkin'?"

Neither you nor the two monkeys are really sure how to respond.

"We can go for walk if we want!" Monkey Maxine pouts.

"We just wanted a break," you start to say, but stop when a slow, menacing chuckle bubbles out of Captain Yogger. From the sinister look in his eye, you're pretty sure you're in the worst trouble of your life.

"It looks like ye be needin' t' be taught a lil' lesson on me rules, aye?"

Monkey Monica lowers her head.

"Aye aye, Captain."

You swallow hard. If the movies are to be believed, you have a pretty good idea of the kind of lessons pirates teach.

EXERCISE #6: RULES

> *"Thar be many rules if ye be wantin' to sail with ol' Yogger LeFossa," the captain whispers in your ear as he forces you back into the classroom. "Ya might not be thinking we pirates be havin' rules, but we do! Fer example, me monkey mates are mine crew, but don't ye be gettin' no ideas fer feeding 'em. Me monkeys are on a strict diet. No bananas, ya hear?"*
>
> *You nod vigorously and hope for a gentle punishment.*
>
> *"Everything okay, Captain?" First Mate Manfred says as Captain Yogger leads you, Monkey Maxine, and Monkey Monica back to your seats.*
>
> *"Nar. These be tryin' t' sneak away from thar werk. Me thinks thay be needin' another lesson on me rules."*
>
> *"Absolutely," First Mate Manfred stands to his feet. "Pay close attention. Rules are important. We have much to discuss."*

As you know, life is full of rules; they are all around us. Math, language, story grammar, and pirate ships all have rules. Even fun and games have rules. If they didn't, you wouldn't know how to play!

Rules help define what can and cannot happen in the story world. Rules govern behavior within the story world.

> Families have rules. Here are a few examples:
> *No shoes in the house.*
> *No games before schoolwork is done.*
> *Speak kindly to each other.*
> *No peanuts because dad is allergic.*
> *Bedtime is 9 p.m. sharp.*
> *No jumping on the couch.*

What are five rules in your family?

1. _____

2. _____

3. _____

4. _____

5. _____

Every story is full of rules. Some are very specific and binding, like the rule: "No napping when there's work to be done." This is a rule of the ship, and someone will wake you up and put you to work if you're caught breaking it. We'll call rules like this "regulations."

Other rules are harder to see. Sometimes this is because they are not announced. "Every Wednesday we dance the jig" is an example of this. No one will tell you about this, but you'll see us following this rule every Wednesday night. The crew sees it as a tradition, and it's what we always do. It's not a regulation kind of rule – you aren't going to get into trouble if you break it – but it's still a rule. It tells what is normal and regular for this crew. We usually call rules like this customs.

Captain Yogger steps in front of your desk and leans in close.

"Listen close, Spat. Some rules be regulations – rules ye best be followin'. Others are just th' way things work on our pirate ship – those are what we be callin' customs," he grabs a paper from First Mate Manfred and slides it in front of you.

"Show me ye be understandin'. Below, circle th' rules that are customs, and scratch yer X on those regulations that are like laws!"

1. No be stickin' yer head in th' mouth of th' kraken (no matter how hard he be tryin' t' convince ye it a fun game).

2. Be waitin' 30 minutes after eatin' a full meal before ye go fer a swim.

3. Keep yer weapons clean an' ready; always be prepared fer an attack!

4. Every mornin' we be exercisin'."

5. Everyone be considered family on th' ship.

6. Everyone be werkin' equally hard on th' ship.

7. Everyone splits th' loot evenly.

8. Ye don't stab others in the back, even if they are yer enemy.

9. If yer caught stealin', ye must be payin' them back.

10. Be sleepin' only after class an' chores be done.

"Ye were no so sure o' th' answers. Tellin' th' difference between customs and regulations is no so easy fer ya, aye, Spat? This bein' 'cause ye are in a strange new place. I bet ye know th' difference between customs and regulations in all th' places you be knowin' well, like at home or in yer world's classroom. When ye are being told a story fer th' first time, ye no usually be knowin' th' difference between customs and regulations. That be part o' th' fun. Is it a custom or regulation t' not stick yer head in a kraken?" Captain Yogger grins are you when you stare back at him blankly.

"I . . . uh . . . " you stumble over your words.

"Ye no so sure, aye? Well, I be tellin' ye, it's a regulation fer you, so no be doing it. Ye'll be findin' out soon enough if it's a regulation fer me or not. Ya har!"

Some rules are the same wherever you go. For example, cars stop at red lights and people use money to buy things at the store. Some rules are based on culture: people from Eastern Osia take off their shoes when entering houses. Other rules only apply to specific locations: there are rules for libraries (no talking) and rules for swimming pools (no running).

Choose one of the following (circle one): library, church, classroom, restaurant, grocery store, movie theater, amusement park, public swimming pool, grandparents' house, skate park, sports stadium. What are 5 rules that exist in this place?

1. _____

2. _____

3. _____

4. _____

5. _____

Choose one of the following (circle one): library, church, classroom, restaurant, grocery store, movie theater, amusement park, public swimming pool, grandparents' house, skate park, sports stadium. What are 5 rules that exist in this place?

1. _____

2. _____

3. _____

4. _____

5. _____

Choose one of the following (circle one): library, church, classroom, restaurant, grocery store, movie theater, amusement park, public swimming pool, grandparents' house, skate park, sports stadium. What are 5 rules that exist in this place?

1. _____

2. _____

3. _____

4. _____

5. _____

Games are full of rules. When you are new to a game, you need to be taught the rules so that you can understand how to play.

Make a list of 16 types of games you know well:

1. _____   9. _____
2. _____   10. _____
3. _____   11. _____
4. _____   12. _____
5. _____   13. _____
6. _____   14. _____
7. _____   15. _____
8. _____   16. _____

Choose a game: _____

Write down 3 rules for this game:

1. _____
   _____

2. _____
   _____

3. _____
   _____

Choose another game: _____

Write down 3 rules for this game:

1. _____
   _____

2. _____
   _____

3. _____
   _____

Choose another game: _____

Write down 3 rules for this game:

1. _____
   _____

2. _____
   _____

3. _____
   _____

Choose another game: _____

Write down 3 rules for this game:

1. _____
   _____

2. _____
   _____

3. _____
   _____

Captain Yogger crosses his arms and stares deep into your eyes.
"Rules be everywhere, not just on me ship. Some even be rulin' th' physical world."
"Like gravity?" Monkey Monica asks.
"Aye. Like gravity," Captain Yogger agrees.
Although you still feel nervous, you're beginning to think that maybe he isn't going to punish you after all.

"What other rules might thar be in th' world, do ya think?" Captain Yogger asks after a brief pause.

What are 5 other rules, like gravity, that govern the physical world?

1. _____

2. _____

3. _____

4. _____

5. _____

Captain Yogger smirks.
"Aye. Yer gettin' it," he turns his back to you and begins pacing around the room.
Monkey Maxine yawns.
"Are we done yet?" she asks impatiently.
Captain Yogger shoots her a dark look that tells you there is still more to do.
"Ye three be thinkin' ye know what is best. Ye be thinkin' ye above me rules. But a good captain don't create rules unless thay be important. Do ye think I be a bad captain?"
Right away, Monkey Monica shakes her head.
"Not at all!" she squeaks.
This makes Captain Yogger laugh.
"Ya har! Ye try t' be gettin' out o' me rules. Let me ask ye somethin' else. Imagine ye be diggin' fer treasure on a hot, desert island. If ye were th' captain, what rules would ye give th' crew? Cross out the rules that no be needed here."

Drink plenty of water.

Don't swim after a meal.

Work in teams of two or three.

Sleep eight hours a day.

Tell the captain if you find something interesting.

Take breaks.

Practice your dance moves twice a day.

Don't eat too much sugar.

Brush your teeth daily.

Share any treasure you find.

Wear a hat.

"Now imagine ye be on a jungle island full of sneaky snakes. Gimme five good rules fer safety and success."

1. _____

2. _____

3. _____

4. _____

5. _____

"Now imagine ye are the captain of me crew. What kind o' rules would ye make, aye?"

1. _____
2. _____
3. _____
4. _____
5. _____

"Yo ho ho!" Captain Yogger grabs his belly and lets out a hearty laugh when you show him what you wrote. "Ye think ye can be a captain with those rules? It be a good thing ye be here. Ye got a lot t' learn, Spat. A lot t' learn."

Without another word, Captain Yogger walks out of the room, repeating your rule number four and laughing to himself.

You look up and see First Mate Manfred. He hands you another piece of paper.

"There's more to do, if you think you can handle it," First Mate Manfred says with a sly grin.

"HEAVE HO!"

Like Captain Yogger did for you, come up with your own scenario and create five rules (either regulations or customs) for that situation.

Scenario: _____
1. _____
2. _____
3. _____
4. _____
5. _____

Scenario: _____
1. _____
2. _____
3. _____
4. _____
5. _____

Think of a specific place: _____

Create rules for that place:
1. _____
2. _____
3. _____
4. _____
5. _____

Create a significant object for that place: _____

Create rules for that significant object:

Example: The treasure chest can only be opened under the light of a full moon.

Example: Only Grandpa Horace can use the gold-plated coffee mug he won in Lost Vegas.

1. _____
2. _____

3. _____

4. _____

5. _____

When Captain Yogger talked about a lesson on rules, you thought he meant he was going to make you walk the plank, or maroon you on an island, or something tortuous maybe. But, nope, apparently he meant just going back to class and doing some more activities.

"Huh," you think to yourself, "maybe this captain isn't so evil after all...."

You start to follow all the monkeys out of the classroom and head toward your bunk for that long awaited nap, when Captain Yogger abruptly steps in front of you.

"Not so fast, Scurvy Spat. Ye owe me a clean floor, yet."

"Ha ha!" you hear the annoying laughter of Missy Monkey as she strolls past.

"What! I was going to bed," you try to protest, but he raises his hook in front of your face and wiggles it back and forth.

"Thar be a problem, Landlubber?"

All you've been able to think about for the last hour was curling up in bed and falling asleep. But, you know you're in no position to bargain. Sleep will just have to wait.

"Aye, aye," you grumble as you shuffle past him and grab the mop.

At least you aren't alone. Monkey Monica and Monkey Maxine have to clean too.

"No fair!" Monkey Maxine sticks her tongue out and crosses her arms as soon as Captain Yogger leaves. "I want to sleep!"

You feel the exact same way, but know that throwing a tantrum won't help, so you start to mop next to Monkey Monica.

"You sure you're his favorite?" you ask when she makes eye contact.

"Hmph!" she turns her face away from you and gives no further response.

CHAPTER ARGH AYE AYE AYE

The next morning, you awake to the cries of "Sail ho!"

You don't quite know all the pirate terms yet, but you recognize this means there's a ship in the distance.

"What's going on?" you ask a monkey named Morgan as you step out onto the deck and into the blinding light of day.

The monkey rolls his eyes at you and grumbles under his breath, "fool-hearty, landlubbing, lard-kisser."

You shrug off his insults and search the horizon for what you expect will be a ship. And sure enough, your eyes spot a small speck far off on the horizon.

"It be Brintish!" Mini Mate cries from his vantage point at the top of the sail. You notice he's holding a golden telescope in his hand.

A few seconds after Mini Mate announces the type of ship, several other monkeys shuffle past you carrying a flag under their arms that resembles the British flag you know – only this one is green and yellow instead of blue and red.

Now you're really confused; the monkeys are covering the Jolly Roger – the classic pirate flag – with the strange British flag!

You notice Monkey Mackenzie standing nearby. He's one of the nicer monkeys from class, so you decide to ask him what's going on.

"We replace the flag," he replies plainly.

"I can tell that much," you frown, "but why?"

"Why? Because Brintish come now. See!" Monkey Mackenzie points toward the distant ship. Sure enough, it appears that the other ship is turning in your direction.

"That's not the British flag, you know," you inform Monkey Mackenzie.

He squints his eyes at you.

"Yes. It Brintish."

You aren't sure if he's pronouncing "British" wrong, or if it's a completely different country. But before you can get any clarity, Monkey Mackenzie laughs at you and jumps away to join the other monkeys, who are now hiding themselves in various corners of the ship.

It doesn't take long before the other ship is close in view. Much to your surprise, it seems they are also flying the strange, green and yellow version of the British flag.

"I guess Brintish must be some other country," you mumble quietly.

Monkey Monica stands at the bow and waves to them with a little, red-spotted handkerchief.

As the ship draws even closer, you notice that it is full of well-dressed humans. Some point at Monkey Monica and chuckle to themselves, while others wave and call things out, like:

"Hello there, little friend!"

"Oh, she's just perfect!"

"My daughter would love one like that!"

Just when you are starting to think Captain Yogger is attempting to find new members for the crew, the newly-hung Brintish flag atop your ship is ripped away by Mini Mate, and the Jolly Roger is exposed once again.

The humans notice it right away and start to scream and beg for mercy.

"It's LeFossa!" one shouts.

"Don't hurt us," another cries, "it's all a misunderstanding!"

One of the men runs to the front and starts to wave a white flag. You recognize that as the symbol of surrender.

"Ya har!" Captain Yogger shouts as he leaps to the front of the deck and flashes an evil grin. "Board that ship, me hearties! It be liberatin' time!"

Twenty-five monkeys burst out of hiding, brandish swords, grab ropes, and swing across to the other ship.

The humans cry and scream as they're tied up, but from what you can tell, none of them are harmed.

At first, you thought that this was a raiding or plundering tactic, but you're surprised to see several of the monkey crew returning with other monkeys in chains.

The ones in chains seem wild and much more like the monkeys you know from your world. They hiss and scream and try to fight back as they're brought onboard Captain Yogger's ship.

"Take em' down below, mates!" Captain Yogger orders.

"Aye, aye!" Mini Mate replies, and he and a few others escort the newly-captured monkeys away.

"LeFossa, please," one of the Brintish women shouts to him, "let us go. We didn't mean any harm."

For some reason, this makes Captain Yogger laugh.

"Well, now, let me think . . ." He pauses for a brief second, then, quite unexpectedly, runs to the railing, leaps off the ship, and lands on theirs with a loud thud. You have no idea how he can move so swiftly with two wooden legs.

He pulls out a long, curved sword and creates sparks with it by dragging it along the deck as he wanders among their crew.

"Thar be no more o' yer kind on me waters, aye? Ye be leavin' now, fer good?"

The captured crew nod their heads vigorously.

"We promise. We'll go!" one of them cries.

Captain Yogger lifts the sword to the chin of the one who spoke, looks him straight in the eye, and sneers.

"An' if ye be lyin'? What then, matey?"

"I p-p-promise!" The man looks like he is about to pass out.

Captain Yogger lets the man fear for his life for a few more seconds before lowering his sword and breaking out into wild laughter. Then, almost as quickly as he boarded them, he leaps off and is back on his own ship.

Then, sitting on the railing, he kicks their ship as hard as he can with his peg leg, causing them to slowly drift away.

"Go back to Gran' Brintian, ye limey gopher-faced, grog snuffers!" Captain Yogger shouts.

EXERCISE #7: SYMBOLISM

A symbol represents something. It stands in the place of something else. Symbols communicate complex things in simple ways.

Stories are full of symbols, just like bananas are full of potassium and tryptophan.

Road signs are a simple type of symbol. A red octagon with the word "STOP" in the middle represents a specific command: stop here. A sign with an airplane and an arrow pointing straight up communicates a message: the airport is ahead. And, of course, everyone knows a skull and crossbones means that us pirates are near!

On the left is a list of symbols, and on the right is a list of things they could represent. Connect the right symbol with the right meaning.

_____ Stop sign   a. No smoking

_____ Green light   b. Sad

_____ Golden M   c. Batman

_____ A smiley face   d. Stop

_____ A black bat in a yellow oval   e. Love

_____ A cigarette with a line through it   f. Superman

_____ A heart   g. Happy

_____ A red "S" inside a diamond   h. Go

_____ A frowny face   i. McDonald's

Mindstorm 10 common symbols on the left and what they represent on the right.

1. _____   _____

2. _____   _____

3. _____   _____

4. _____   _____

5. _____   _____

6. _____   _____

7. _____   _____

8. _____   _____

9. _____   _____

10. _____   _____

Holidays are loaded with symbols; Christmas is stuffed with them. Write a list of symbols for Christmas. I'll give you a few to get you started.

1. Decorated tree
2. Red and green
3. Mistletoe
4. _____
5. _____
6. _____
7. _____

8. _____
9. _____
10. _____
11. _____
12. _____
13. _____
14. _____

WORDS AS SYMBOLS

Symbols enable communication. The word "apple" is a symbol of a specific kind of fruit. A word isn't the actual thing itself, but a kind of arrow pointing to the thing.

Symbols like "apple" are human inventions. The French invented a different symbol for the same thing, "pomme." Sign language has a hand motion – a visual symbol – for apple.

Invent three different symbols for communicating one of the following words: fire, flower, fairy, fart, frog, feather.

You can use letters, symbols, drawings, sounds, hand signals, or anything else you can imagine.

Example: "fire" = "VVV" or "Haught" or "Theoplasmorphic Conflagmyosis"

Word: _____
    1. _____
    2. _____
    3. _____

Word: _____
    1. _____
    2. _____
    3. _____

Symbols enable communication, but only if people understand what those symbols mean. The symbols you created above might not communicate the message you intend. Thus, if I invent the word "VVV" I will need to find a way to explain to others that "VVV" means fire. I may also need to find a way to convince you a bunch of "V"s is a good way to symbolize fire. This is what all authors must do with the symbols they use in their stories.

Symbols only have power when someone understands what they mean.

Circle all of the symbols that you understand the meaning of:

Transfiguration	Pieces of eight	Opice
Bonjour	Muang thai	Frindle
Antidisestablishmentarianism	Pinyin system	Gazette
Lymph	Gethsemene	Bon Jovi
Somatic sense	Evapotranspiration	Hornswaggle
Solenoid	Cordellia	Meddachschlop
Hydraulique	Freude	Ennui
Moraine	Feliz	Faux pas

The symbols you didn't circle are examples of symbols that exist in the world that you don't understand. The meaning of that symbol has already been created, you just don't know what it means. (Believe it or not, those are all real words.) Very often, when we ask, "What is that?" "What does that mean?" "Can you explain that to me?" or "What is she saying?" we are trying to understand some symbol.

MULTIPLE MEANINGS

Sometimes, one symbol can mean different things. The color green can mean all sorts of things. When we see a green light at a traffic intersection, we understand it means: "Go." A green light on a computer power cord usually means "fully charged." A recent meaning for green is "earth-friendly." Someone who is new to the sea is often called "green." People can also be "green with jealousy."

Choose a color: _____ List a few different meanings it symbolizes:

1. _____

2. _____

3. _____

Choose another color: _____ List a few different meanings it symbolizes:

1. _____

2. _____

3. _____

Color can mean different things for different cultures. In Northern Canmerico, white is the color of weddings. But in Eastern Osia, they wear white to funerals.

What do the following symbols mean to you?

1. A heart: Romanic love / Valentine's Day / Feelings / Life

2. A smiley-face emoji: Happiness / Joy / Support / Welcome

3. A siren and flashing red lights: _____ / _____ / _____

4. A stuffed animal: _____ / _____ / _____

5. Apple pie: _____ / _____ / _____

6. An American flag: _____ / _____ / _____

7. Summer vacation: _____ / _____ / _____

8. Turkey: _____ / _____ / _____

9. A dog: _____ / _____ / _____

10. Computers: _____ / _____ / _____

Symbols are everywhere. Even our own signature is a symbol we have created to represent our name!

Write your signature five different ways:

CREATING SYMBOLS

Writing a story is a great way for a person to create symbols because stories are full of symbols. In fact, a story is a symbol. It is a very complex symbol that is built by the author using a lot of smaller symbols. This is because humans and talking monkeys need symbols to communicate.

An easy way to create a new symbol is to create a new word, like we did above with "VVV" for fire. One easy way to create new words is to take two existing words and smash them together.

For example, take the color "purple" and "mouse" and squeeze them together.

Ta-da: you've now got "purplemouse."

Take the word "pirate" and the body part "heart" and you have "pirateheart."

It's up to you, the symbol creator, to define what the new word represents. Purplemouse might represent a strange breed of mouse, or be a term for a mouse that ran up against the edge of a rainbow. Pirateheart sounds like a good description for a greedy, selfish, pirate-like heart (that is, unless you're the good kind of pirate, like us).

Make a list of random words.

1. _____
2. _____
3. _____
4. _____
5. _____
6. _____
7. _____
8. _____
9. _____
10. _____

11. _____
12. _____
13. _____
14. _____
15. _____
16. _____
17. _____
18. _____
19. _____
20. _____

Now, combine these words to create ten new words.

Example: pirate + heart = pirateheart

1. _____
2. _____
3. _____
4. _____
5. _____

6. _____
7. _____
8. _____
9. _____
10. _____

Take 5 of these crazy new words that you have created and make up a definition to tell what the words mean:

Example: Pirate + heart = Pirateheart = a pirate's tattoo; or the spot where a pirate buries their stolen treasure; or someone who has a greedy, selfish heart.

1. _____
2. _____
3. _____
4. _____
5. _____

"HEAVE HO!"

Did you know that charades is a way of communicating purely through physical symbols? Ancient Egyptian hieroglyphics are symbols too. Most of the monkey crew still use a picture language called Monkeyscript. Instead of writing words in English with an alphabet, like you do, they use pictures to say what they mean.

Imagine you need to write a note to one of my monkey brethren (they don't write or read as well as I do).

Write a sentence you might find in a letter, then rewrite the sentence in Monkeyscript (create pictures to communicate the sentence).

English: _____

Monkeyscript: _____

Often a significant object can be symbolic (though it doesn't have to be). In *The Wizard of Oz*, Dorothy's ruby slippers are a symbol that she was never very far from home. In *Winnie the Pooh*, the honey pot is a symbol that points to Pooh Bear's great hunger.

Think of five significant objects from books or movies you know well. For each one, tell what you think it could be symbolic of:

1. _____ : _____
2. _____ : _____
3. _____ : _____
4. _____ : _____
5. _____ : _____

People do not always agree on what symbols mean. But, this is one reason symbols in stories can be so powerful. They are flexible. They can change. They can look like one thing to one person and something else to another. Symbols allow different people to see stories in different ways.

Circle the symbol that <u>you</u> think is the best of the three options:

1. If someone is lost in the dark, (a flashlight / a friend / the North Star) might be a symbol of hope.

2. For a ship lost at sea, a (lighthouse / map / mermaid) is a symbol of a comfort.

3. If you were wanting give someone a symbol of friendship, you might give them a (car / friendship necklace / punch).

Circle the meaning that <u>you</u> think is the best of the three options:

1. A hug is a symbol of (encouragement / love / protection).

2. Some people consider fireworks a symbol of (freedom / excitement / wastefulness).

3. Fire is a symbol of (love / anger / purification).

You see? Symbols can point to many different things.

Fill in the blank with no help from me.

1. A car is a symbol of _____.

2. A big house is considered a symbol of _____.

3. Gargoyles were placed on buildings because they were a symbol of _____.

4. In stories written for senior citizens, children are a symbol of _____.

5. Zombies walking around a shopping mall are a symbol of _____.

List some possible symbols for the following:

1. Freedom: _____

2. Revenge: _____

3. Foolishness: _____

4. Envy: _____

5. Absent-mindedness_____

RAISE THE ANCHOR AND SET SAIL

You know what to do here. Write a story of your own. Was there a symbol that stuck out to you? I sometimes begin a story by thinking of a problem that a character has and what they do in order to solve it. You're on the open sea, go wherever your imagination takes you.

_____

_____

_____

_____

_____

_____

_____

_____

_____

_____

_____

_____

_____

_____

_____

_____

_____

_____

_____

_____

_____

_____

_____

_____

CHAPTER AYE AVAST

That night, you gather with the other monkeys in the mess hall for what appears to be another meal of nachos, noodles, and nectarines. The cook – so you're told – is a monkey named Norman Nopants. Apparently he used to cook at some of the fanciest restaurants in the world, but could never keep a job because he refused to cook anything unless it started with "n."

But here, Captain Yogger doesn't allow anyone to be picky or complain about the food. So Norman is free to cook whatever "n" foods he can think of, and many of the monkeys force the meal down their throats with a look of misery.

"You don't like it?" you ask Missy Monkey.

"Nah," she frowns, "I miss bananas."

You nod, understanding how they must feel. You don't particularly care for bananas, but you're getting fairly sick of foods beginning with "n." You don't quite understand how, but there seems to be an endless supply of those types of food on this ship.

"If you aren't going to finish that, I'll eat yours!" You can barely understand Monkey Maxine because her mouth is so jammed full of food.

"You so disgusting," Monkey Monica grumbles, "how can you eat so much of this?"

Monkey Maxine shrugs.

"Just hungry."

After forcing yourself to eat a few more bites, you slide Monkey Maxine your plate and watch as she greedily adds it to her stack.

"Thanks!" she grins as you quietly excuse yourself from the table and decide to go back to your room.

You don't get far, though, because as soon as you pass by the kitchen, a thick, accented voice calls to you:

"Nyet mood to eat, da, Scurvy Spat?"

You turn and see a monkey wearing a tall, white chef hat, a white chef's jacket, and white underwear.

"You must be . . . Norman Nopants?" you ask.

"Da. What gave Norman away?" he replies in all seriousness.

You smile, thinking it must be a joke.

"I'm sure the meal is great. I just . . . don't feel terribly hungry right now."

"Nyet? Maybe eat nugget? Norman bring nuts?"

"No, no. I'm all right."

You turn to leave and follow through with your original plan, but something about the openness in Norman's voice causes you to hesitate. He might be a good one to talk to.

"What happened with the other ship earlier? Why were there monkeys in chains on board?"

"Ah," Norman crosses his arms, "they monkey slave. Need time to calm down and be one of crew. So stay in bottom deck for work with Monkey Mackenzie to be whole again."

"Monkey slaves?" You've never heard of such a thing. "Why would anyone do that?"

"Those people – they nyet nice people. They rich by get, sell monkey slave. Norman lose many brother and sister to slaver boat. That why Norman love Yogger; he no slave Norman."

"What do you mean," you start to wonder if maybe you've misjudged the captain and his monkey pirates, "were you all slaves?"

"Many come from slaver. See, monkey mates born smelly. Other monkeys on Monkey Mountain nyet like monkey mates because bad smell, so send them away. But, most Captains nyet nice to monkeys. Many try to steal and make slave. Yogger different. He say he want all to be free. So Norman and monkey mates follow him. Yogger good man. He nyet care for money. He leave behind to sail."

"What do you mean?" You find it hard to believe that a pirate captain wouldn't care about money.

"Da, da. He use to be prince of kingdom, believe Norman or nyet," Norman shrugs, "but that were long time ago."

"A prince?" The thought is so absurd that you feel like he's trying to play some type of joke on you.

"Da, da. Prince Eli of Emerald Island. He were born with problem. Bad breath. Norman sure you notice that."

You have to cover your mouth to keep from laughing.

"Yeah. I noticed."

"Cause his breath were so strange and foul, he not fit in with others in his kingdom," Norman Nopants says as he scratches his back with a wooden spoon. "He spend many days in tower of castle, to read stories about great pirates. One day, he get tired of reading, and decide to take to sea. Leave whole life behind and be pirate himself. "

"Are you serious?" You can hardly believe it. "But he was a prince! Why would he want to leave that life?"

"He fell to love pirate code – honor for thieves, brotherhood, strength. Norman guess Captain Yogger think life better as pirate than prince. It true too."

You want to ask Norman more questions, but, before you can say anything, he turns his back to you and shuffles into the kitchen.

"Wait!" you cry out, but he doesn't stop.

"Nyet. Norman have work time now. Bye-bye," Norman mumbles.

"One last question, please!" you can't help yourself, and ask the thing that's been bothering you since you first heard about him, "Why are you called Norman when all the other monkey mates have 'M' names?"

This makes Norman stop and scoff.

"Norman tell you two backstories today. Norman did nyet tell you Norman backstory," he replies cryptically, then looks over his shoulder, winks, and disappears into the kitchen.

EXERCISE #8: BACKSTORY

We experience a long string of events over the course of our lives stretching as far back into the past as we can remember. We call this history. _In story, the string of events that took place in the past is called a backstory; it is the story that led up to the story being told, and it explains why things are as they are in the story world._

Usually we talk about this in terms of character: a character's backstory tells us why and how the character is the way they are. But it is also true of the entire story world. Everything has a reason why it is the way it is; backstory gives the author the reasons why.

1. Think of something you don't like: _____

Give a simple reason for why you don't like it: _____

_____

_____

2. Now think of something you do like: _____

Give a simple reason from the past (your backstory) for why you like it: _____

_____

_____

3. Think of something else you don't like: _____

Give a simple reason for why you don't like it: _____

_____

_____

4. Think of something else you do like: _____

Give a simple reason from the past (your backstory) for why you like it: _____

_____

_____

You are, right now, in a certain place. How did you come to be there?

Where are you – Scurvy Spat – right now?

     On a pirate ship.

Where were you before this and what were you doing?

     I was in the ocean, trying to keep from drowning.

Before that, _I was sliding through some kind of magic portal or something._

Before that, _I was in my bed falling into a nice, peaceful sleep._

Before that, I was _____.

Before that, I was _____.

Before that, I was _____.

Before that, I was _____.

Before that, I was _____.

Each step answered the question, "what happened just before?" In the next example, you will choose steps that go farther back in history. You'll be answering the question, "what major things happened in the years before?"

For example, perhaps you are wondering how our Captain Yogger came to command this ship?

> He was a pirate captain, and before this he was a pirate.
>
> Before that, he was a prisoner of the dreaded Pirate Captain Redbeard.
>
> Before that, he was a stowaway on Black-Eye the Third's ship!
>
> Before that, he was in exile.
>
> Before that, he was Prince Eli of Emerald Island.
>
> Before that, he was just a stinky baby.

Name the place where are you are right now: _____
What significant things in your life happened before this?

1. _____

2. _____

3. _____

4. _____

5. _____

6. _____

7. _____

8. _____

9. _____

10. _____

SIMPLE BACKSTORY

Sometimes the reasons or events that make us like or dislike something are simple. For example, I hate coconut football. Why? I'll let you guess. Which of the following backstories do you think led me to feel this way?

1. When I was a small monkey, I ate a coconut every single day! It was my favorite food, until one day I got greedy and ate too many of them all at once, and it made me terribly sick. Ever since I can't look at one without feeling ill.

2. My dad and I used to watch coconut football every week. These are some of my happiest memories with him. But after he died, whenever I went to go watch a coconut football game, people threw coconuts at me because of my stink. I didn't have my dad to protect me anymore. So, I stopped going.

3. When I was a small monkey, I went to watch a friend play coconut football. and the coconut was kicked out of bounds, hit me in the face, and broke my nose!

Any one of these three things could be a backstory that explained why I don't like coconut football. Which one do you think is true? _____

1. Describe something from your past (your backstory) that caused you to be scared.

_____

_____

Would you still feel scared if that same thing happened to you today? _____

2. Describe something from your past (your backstory) that caused you to be joyful.

_____

_____

Would you still feel joyful if that same thing happened to you today? _____

3. Describe something from your past (your backstory) that caused you to be angry.

_____

_____

Would you still become angry if that same thing happened to you today? _____

4. Describe something from your past (your backstory) that caused you to be surprised.

_____

_____

Would you still be surprised if that same thing happened to you today? _____

COMPLEX BACKSTORY

Sometimes, the reasons for why things are the way they are today are simple, but other times they are more complex. Getting my nose smashed by a coconut at a game made me hate coconut football. It's a simple reason. But, you want to know why I love Captain Yogger?

I'll tell you, but let's make it an exercise. Underline every moment in my backstory that you think is significant to me serving on this ship:

"When I was a wee monkey, I had a nice mom who made sure I had lots of friends. But, that was a challenge for her because I was stinky from birth. Really stinky. And many of the monkeys who claimed to be my friends started to make fun of me the older we got. It was bad enough to get hit in the nose by a coconut by accident, but when monkeys started throwing coconuts at me to get me to stay away, I ran.

"I was lonely in Port Latundan, but then I saw a big ship arrive. That's when I met Captain Yogger. He took one smell of me and, instead of running away, he gave me a chance. I thought it was a trick at first, but then I smelled his breath and realized he was stinky too! And so I became the first monkey to join his crew.

"He was hard, but fair. He taught me everything I know, and even though I couldn't pull my weight in the beginning, he gave me a share in all the loot. And he never made fun of my stink. Now, I'm his right hand, and you'd see me walk the plank before I let anyone hurt him!"

See? I could have given you a simple reason: the captain treats me well. But instead, I gave a lot more details and reasons, which make a simple backstory more complex.

1. Think of something else that you like. Think of something that has a more complex backstory (it has many reasons from the past why you like it): _____

Describe the reasons why you came to like this thing:

_____

_____

_____

_____

2. Now, think of something that you <u>don't</u> like that has a more complex backstory:

_____

Describe the reasons why you came to dislike this thing:

_____

_____

_____

_____

Backstory can explain many other things. It can explain the reasons why certain things make you afraid and other things make you happy. It can help you understand why you are the way you are. It's also a way authors come to understand why their characters are the way they are.

Let's say you want to create a character who has a fear of spiders. What are some things in that character's backstory that might have caused them to be this way?

1. They were bitten by a spider when they were young.

2. Their big brother had a pet spider collection and would hide spiders in their bed.

3. The Spiderman movies gave them nightmares.

4. _____

5. _____

6. _____

7. _____

Name a fear you have and describe how you came to fear that thing.

Example: I'm scared of people jumping out at me in the dark.

How did I come to have this fear? When I was five years old, we went trick-or-treating, and someone jumped out from behind a gate and yelled. It terrified me!

Name something that you are afraid of: _____

Describe how you came to have that fear:

_____

_____

_____

Name another fear you have: _____

Describe an experience you had that produced that fear:

_____

_____

_____

CHARACTERIZATIONS

Backstory can also explain why a character has what we call characterizations. (There will be an entire lesson on characterizations later.)

There might be a girl who has a scar across her cheek. This is a characterization, and so there is probably a reason in her backstory that explains how she came to have this scar.

Character: A girl with a scar across her cheek.

Describe 3 different backstories that led to that character's characterization:

> *Example 1: She was taken hostage by Sweetish Pirates. To escape from the room she was locked in, she broke the window and cut her face on the jagged glass on the way out.*

> *Example 2: Her great, great, great grandmother, a famous head-hunter, had a distinctive scar, so all of her female descendants have been given the same scar in order for everyone to know who they are.*

> *Example 3: She was born with a lump on her cheek, and as she was from a poor family in southern Osia, her family could not afford to pay a doctor. Thus the "surgery" to remove the lump left a noticeable scar.*

Here are some other characters:

A boy who always wears shorts, even though he lives in Minnesota

A 63-year-old man who has braces

A 92-year-old woman with Alzheimer's who always has a daisy in her hair

An 18-year-old boy who always has a golf ball in his hand or pocket

A 12-year-old girl who has 125 signed baseball cards

A 16-year-old boy who lives alone in a house with 12 bedrooms

A 15-year-old monkey who works for an evil pirate captain

Choose one of the characters from above: _____

Describe 3 different backstories that led to who they are.

1. _____

_____

_____

2. _____

_____

_____

3. _____

_____

_____

Do the same with another character from above: _____

1. _____

_____

_____

2. _____

_____

_____

3. _____

_____

_____

Do the same with another character from above: _____

1. _____

_____

_____

2. _____

_____

_____

3. _____

_____

_____

"HEAVE HO!"

Write the name of a character you know well (from a book or movie): _____

What caused them to be the way that they are? Give 5 reasons (simple or complex) for why they do what they do, like what they like, or look the way they do:

1. _____
2. _____
3. _____
4. _____
5. _____

Mini Mate likes to dress and talk like Captain Yogger. Why do you think that is? Take a guess at what his backstory might be. Give 5 reasons (simple or complex) for why he dresses, acts, and talks the way he does:

1. _____
2. _____
3. _____
4. _____
5. _____

Create a character: give them a name and some distinguishing feature.

Name: _____

Distinguishing feature: _____

Now, give that character a backstory – simple or complex – for why they have that distinguishing feature.

_____

_____

_____

Bonus: can you connect your character's distinguishing feature to a fear they have?

_____

_____

_____

CHAPTER AVAST

As you walk toward the kitchen to see what "n"-named food Norman has prepared for you tonight, you hear the sound of screaming from down a set of nearby stairs.

Part of you is afraid to go that deep into the ship. You've heard rumors the ship holds lots of secrets, especially the lower parts. But, the screams could mean trouble, so you take a deep breath and nervously descend the steps.

Once at the bottom, you see rows and rows of cages full of the monkeys rescued from the Brintish ship. They are no longer in chains, but still locked up. They're completely wild, leaping around their cages and screaming at the top of their lungs.

In front of one cage stand Mini Mate and Monkey Mo Mo, two of your classmates. Monkey Mo Mo is currently trying to feed a plate of noodles to one of the monkeys, but the monkey keeps slapping the plate away, screaming, and throwing the noodles around.

"Nar! She no bein' ready yet," Mate says to Monkey Mo Mo.

"She scared. She don't know me no more."

"Aye. But she will. Be actin' just like ye with me last year," Mini Mate affirms.

Just as you decide this doesn't concern you and you should probably leave, you step on a creaky board, and the two monkeys spin around to see you standing there.

"Oh," you try to smile, "hey guys."

"What ye be wantin', Spat?" Mini Mate hisses.

"I just . . . heard screaming," you stumble over your words.

"It okay," Monkey Mo Mo says sadly, "this be our sister Maya, in cage."

"Your sister?" you repeat.

"Aye," Mini Mate explains, "long ago, we three be taken from our home an' be made slaves. Cap'n Yogger find me first and relearn me t' speak," Mini Mate explains. "I be tryin' t' find an' rescue me family since so they have thar life again."

"You were once wild like this?" You find that hard to believe. The monkeys in the cages are so much crazier than the monkey mates.

"Aye, slavers turned us wild," Monkey Mo Mo nods. "I still have nightmares." He raises his hands to his face and starts to whimper.

"I'm sorry," you say as you reach your hand out to try and comfort Monkey Mo Mo, but he pushes you away and hisses.

"We no trust ye yet," Mini Mate warns. "Ye still be human. Human make monkey slave!" "I'm not like that," you insist, "I would never do that."

The dark scowls of the two monkeys tell you they aren't convinced.

"Th' only reason ye still be livin' is 'cause Cap'n like ye," Mini Mate states. "Ye connected to him. He my boss. So I let ye live."

You swallow the lump growing in your throat.

"Thank you," it feels weird to say it; you've never thanked someone for letting you live before.

Mini Mate grunts and then turns his back to you again and the two monkeys resume trying to feed their wild sister. But once again, she knocks it aside.

"She probably doesn't realize it's safe to eat," you suggest warily.

The other two monkeys scoff.

"We know what we doin', Spat," Mini Mate crosses his arms. "Go away. This be monkey business."

You consider just leaving and letting them do it on their own, but just then, the wild monkey named Maya throws a clump of noodles through the cage. They land with a splat at your feet.

You bend down, pick them up, and take a step toward the cage.

"Hey!" Monkey Mo Mo cries. "Stop! You scare her! Human scary!"

You ignore him, lock eyes with the caged monkey, and reluctantly lift the noodles to your mouth. Despite not feeling much desire for noodles, you take a bite in hope that she'll understand it's food and safe to eat.

She tilts her head curiously as you chew; despite being plain, the noodles are actually kind of good, and you let out a sigh of contentment.

"Mmmmmmm."

You then extend your hand with the noodles toward Monkey Maya.

She jumps away from you, then, slowly takes a few steps closer to the cage.

"Okay. Yummy!" you try to reassure her with kind words as you slurp another noodle into your mouth.

Monkey Maya hesitates, then reaches out and grabs the noodles out of your hand and takes a bite.

"I no believe it," Mini Mate says to Monkey Mo Mo, whose mouth is hanging open in shock.

"See? She didn't understand it was food and safe to eat," you explain, feeling quite proud of yourself for getting the wild monkey to trust you.

"Hmmmm," Mini Mate gradually uncrosses his arms. "Ye might no be so bad after all," he admits at last.

You can't help but grin.

EXERCISE #9: CONNECTIONS

It's a writer's job to establish connections between the various elements of the story to create a whole. _Connections are all the ways different parts of a story come together._ An easy way to demonstrate how this works is a family tree.

List the first names of 10 people in your family.

1. _____

2. _____

3. _____

4. _____

5. _____

6. _____

7. _____

8. _____

9. _____

10. _____

Someone who doesn't know you will not understand how these names are connected.

A family tree is an illustration of the connections between family members where each connecting line describes a specific relationship.

Using the names you listed above, draw a picture of your family tree. Write the relationship on the lines that connect everyone. (For example: mother-son, father-daughter, brother-sister, sister-sister, aunt-niece, grandmother-granddaughter…)

A family tree is like a web that shows the different relationships – connections – between the people in a family. Another kind of web might illustrate how we came to be connected to someone or something. Let's take the example of friends.

List 5 of your friends:

1. _____

2. _____

3. _____

4. _____

5. _____

This time, we already know that your connection to these people is friendship. But we don't know *how* you came to be a friend. Take a look at Jon and his friends:

Jon's friends

> *Jared – met in history class*
>
> *Joey – were on the same sports team*
>
> *Jana – the sister of Joey*
>
> *Justin – met at church*
>
> *Jenn – ride the same school bus*

This shows Jon's friends and what created each connection. See how each of Jon's friends are connected by different things? It could be a person, an organization, an event, a common interest, a place, or anything.

List 5 of your friends plus how you came to be friends:

1. _____

2. _____

3. _____

4. _____

5. _____

We have connections with everyone we come in contact with. Your family and friends are strong connections. But, there are also innumerable little connections. You make a connection with a complete stranger when you look at one another. You may never see them ever again, but for a brief moment there was a very weak connection. In between there are connections with all kinds of people like your teachers, the parents of your friends, and your neighbors. Life is full of connections.

In the space below, write your name in the middle, then write the names of as many people as you can think of all around it. Then, draw a line connecting their names to yours and on that line write how you are connected.

Monkey Monica is friends with Monkey Maxine. They are connected through Captain Yogger's ship. But they have more that connects them. Check off anything in the following list that you think connects these two:

They both want to get out of chores.

They are both hard workers.

Their names both start with "M".

They're both girls.

They both think they're Captain Yogger's favorite.

They both have many monkey siblings.

They both admire Captain Yogger.

They both love the food Norman Nopants makes.

Choose a friend from the list you made and write several ways you are connected:

Friend: _____

1. _____

2. _____

3. _____

4. _____

5. _____

Friend: _____

1. _____

2. _____

3. _____

4. _____

5. _____

CONNECTED BY ACTIVITIES

We are not only connected to people. We can be connected to anything. Let's look at hobbies or activities in terms of a web of connection.

Love of baseball can connect someone to many different things, including people, objects, organizations, events, and ideas. Mark the items on this list that someone who loves baseball might be connected to:

The Punchberg Pirates	Swimming laps
Little League	Baseball hats
Sword-fighting	Watching the World Series on TV
Going to games with Grandpa	Writing letters
Playing catch with my friends	Wholesome values
Baseball cards	Washing the car
Eating tacos	Peanuts
Singing songs	Crackerjacks

Think of a hobby or activity you enjoy: _____

List at least 10 people / objects / stores / organizations / events / ideas that connect you to that hobby or activity:

1. _____   6. _____
2. _____   7. _____
3. _____   8. _____
4. _____   9. _____
5. _____   10. _____

Think of another hobby or activity you enjoy: _____

List at least 10 people / objects / stores / organizations / events / ideas that connect you to that hobby or activity:

1. _____   6. _____
2. _____   7. _____
3. _____   8. _____
4. _____   9. _____
5. _____   10. _____

CONNECTED BY LOCATION

A road map is a visual picture of how locations are connected to one another.

There can be big distances (like the space between Northern Canmerico, the Brintish Isles, and Eastern Osia) and there can be small distances (the distance from my bedroom to the front door of the house).

Think of a place you know well, such as your hometown, your state, your backyard, anywhere at all. Draw a map of how the things in it connect to one another:

A map shows how places or things are connected to each other spatially. People can be connected to places as well. Just like you saw with friendships, you can be connected to a place through other people, objects, events, or situations.

Name 6 places that you go to regularly:

1. _____
2. _____
3. _____

4. _____
5. _____
6. _____

Who or what connected you / introduced you to each one? Draw a web to show how you connected with these places.

BUILDING

Whenever you build or put something together, you are taking different parts and connecting them in a way that transforms them into a whole.

Imagine your friend comes up to you and asks, "do you want to build a snowmonkey?" Together you roll the snowballs, find a button for a nose, and add some coal. You might even add a red scarf and sticks for arms. Put together the right way, you've got a great looking snowmonkey. But, put together incorrectly, you've got nothing but a snowy mess.

Most things around us are made up of parts. All of the connections add up to the whole. For example, if you connect a beef patty, a bun, pickles, lettuce, tomato, and cheese together in the right way, the result is a _____.

In order to have a working pirate ship, you need a few things. Cross off the items on the list that are not needed for a pirate ship, and add 5 more things that are.

Frame	Speakers	Crew	1. _____
Tires	Mast	Rowing oars	2. _____
Watermelons	Ink	Cannons	3. _____
Wheel	Sails	Paper	4. _____
Rudder	Chocolate	Plank	5. _____

Think of an object: _____

List the parts that object is made of (add more lines if you need them):

1. _____
2. _____
3. _____
4. _____
5. _____

Think of another object: _____

List the parts that object is made of (add more lines if you need them):

1. _____
2. _____
3. _____
4. _____
5. _____

Think of another object: _____

List the parts that object is made of (add more lines if you need them):

1.   _____

2. _____

3. _____

4. _____

5. _____

There are often connections between significant objects and characters. For example, my stuffed monkey makes me feel happy because my mom gave it to me when I was born. But that same monkey would make Monkey Mo Mo sad, because it would remind him of his missing little sister.

Create some significant objects:

1. _____   4. _____

2. _____   5. _____

3. _____

Create some characters:

1. _____   4. _____

2. _____   5. _____

3. _____

Create some emotions:

1. _____   4. _____

2. _____   5. _____

3. _____

Now connect them.

Object: _____ + Character: _____ + Emotion_____

Write a sentence that describes this connection: _____

_____

Object: _____ + Character: _____ + Emotion_____

Write a sentence that describes this connection: _____

_____

Object: _____ + Character: _____ + Emotion_____

Write a sentence that describes this connection: _____

_____

"HEAVE HO!"

Ready for more?

Connections can be made in all kinds of ways.

Circle "True" or "False":

1. Connections can be made between people. (T / F)

2. We can see what connects people. (T / F)

3. Connections are not important to a story. (T / F)

4. Places cannot be connected. (T / F)

5. The only way places can be connected is by distance. (T / F)

6. People can be connected to those places in different ways. (T / F)

7. Activities and experiences do not connect us to people, places, things or ideas. (T / F)

8. Individual parts are connected and make a whole. (T / F)

Bonus:

Write the name of one of your favorite stories: _____

List the names of characters in that story:

1. _____

2. _____

3. _____

4. _____

5. _____

List some locations:

1. _____

2. _____

3. _____

4. _____

5. _____

List some significant objects from the story:

1. _____

2. _____

3. _____

4. _____

5. _____

List some activities the characters do:

1. _____

2. _____

3. _____

4. _____

5. _____

Draw a web of connections between all of these characters, places/settings, significant objects and activities. Draw lines of connection between items, and on those lines, write a description of the connection.

SCRATCH YER NOGGIN'

So far, you've learned about the different elements that go into world creating: setting, events, significant objects, worldlings, rules, backstory, values and symbolism.

Events happen when setting (time and place) connect with an activity. Come up with some events and show the time, place and activity that are connected:

Event: A birthday party

Time: Noon

Place: My house

Activity: Coconut football

Event: _____

Time: _____

Place: _____

Activity: _____

Event: _____

Time: _____

Place: _____

Activity: _____

Event: _____

Time: _____

Place: _____

Activity: _____

There can be a connection between a character's physical features and their backstory. (For example, Captain LeFossa has two peg legs because he lost them to a kraken many years ago.)

Captain Yogger has made some interesting friends. Take one of the following pirate friends of his and think about their physical features. Come up with a backstory for that pirate. Why does he/she look the way they do?

1. Pirate Riley Leaper

    Dyed blonde hair

    Tattoo of a kraken on back

    Refuses to wear shoes

2. Pirate Jenny Power

    Short, spiky hair

    Dark eye makeup

    Wears black gloves

3. Pirate Parry Swordsmither

    Has a parrot on each shoulder

    Grows a long, twirly mustache

    Sleeps with one eye open

4. Pirate Ricky Pickle McGrubber

    Often turns green when on the sea

    Has hairy arms

    Is three feet tall

Pirate: _____

Backstory:_____

_____

_____

_____

_____

Pirate: _____

Backstory:_____

_____

_____

_____

_____

The author takes all the different elements that go into a story and connects them in order to build a vibrant and whole story world.

EXERCISE #10: PROBLEMS AND THE ACT OF VILLAINY

Stories, like life, are full of problems. Think of a problem as something that causes someone to take action.

Make a list of problems. Think of every kind of problem you can imagine.

1. Maxine ate my list of 20 problems.
2. Bananas make me smell weird.
3. Getting lost in the Archipelagos.
4. _____
5. _____
6. _____
7. _____
8. _____
9. _____
10. _____

11. _____
12. _____
13. _____
14. _____
15. _____
16. _____
17. _____
18. _____
19. _____
20. _____

Some problems are enormous. Think of some things that, if they happened, would be or create a huge problem.

1. Nuclear war.
2. A disease kills all banana trees.
3. A kraken attacks a helpless ship.
4. _____
5. _____

6. _____
7. _____
8. _____
9. _____
10. _____

Some problems are so small they don't seem like problems at all. But remember, anything that causes someone to take action is a problem.

1. Nature calls. Time to visit the poop deck.
2. My leg itches.
3. The flowers on the table are wilting.
4. _____
5. _____

6. _____
7. _____
8. _____
9. _____
10. _____

PHYSICAL

There are problems that affect our physical body. Fill in the missing word(s) in the following sentences.

Jennifer broke her _____ and can't go to the dance.

I'm so hungry, I want to eat a _____.

Monkey M slipped on a _____ and bumped his _____. Now he can't remember his name!

I fell in the _____ and my favorite _____ is filthy.

Come up with six physical problems, like the ones above.

1. _____
2. _____
3. _____
4. _____
5. _____
6. _____

EMOTIONAL

Other problems are emotional in nature.

I'm feeling _____, because I'm all alone.

After my friend watched a horror movie, she was too _____ to go to sleep.

I forgot to pack my _____, so I've been _____ my entire vacation.

No one _____ the things I'm trying to say.

Come up with six emotional problems, like the ones above.

1. _____
2. _____
3. _____
4. _____
5. _____
6. _____

SOCIAL

Problems can be social in nature.

Nancy put _____ down the back of Jim's shirt at lunchtime yesterday.

Hai choked on a _____ and spit it out into Grover's _____.

Kimmy refused to go to the _____ with Jordan because a _____ was hanging out of his nose.

Heidi dared Fran to kiss a frog, but she _____ instead and so Heidi was _____.

Create your own social problems.

1. _____
2. _____
3. _____
4. _____
5. _____
6. _____

There are social problems that affect an entire society, like drunken sailing, monkey slavery, and piracy. List some others:

1. Bad breath
2. Littering
3. Slipping on a banana peel
4. _____
5. _____
6. _____
7. _____
8. _____
9. _____
10. _____
11. _____
12. _____

Sometimes, something that does not affect you will be a problem for someone else. For example, most monkeys can eat bananas without any problems, but that's not true for us. Or, if you take a test on a subject you know a lot about, passing that test will not be a problem. If Norman asked you to cook dinner tonight, would it be a problem for you? Would your cooking cause a problem for us?

Make a list of things that are not a problem for you, but might be problems for others.

1. Eating broccoli
2. Riding a bicycle with no hands
3. Speaking like a pirate
4. _____
5. _____
6. _____
7. _____
8. _____
9. _____
10. _____
11. _____
12. _____

Problems cause someone to take action. On the left is a list of problems and on the right are some characters. Write the letter or draw a line connecting each problem to the character most likely to consider it a problem and take actions to solve it.

_____ Strange looking bones are dug up.
_____ There is no more honey.
_____ Pirates steal all the bananas.
_____ A house catches on fire.
_____ Aliens land with really big weapons.
_____ A tree fell on my bike.
_____ A child tripped and broke his leg.
_____ Green jelly beans taste like oranges.
_____ An essay for school is due tomorrow.

a. Winnie the Pooh
b. A student
c. A mountain biker
d. The jelly-bean factory workers
e. Paleontologists
f. Firefighters
g. Monkeys
h. The military
i. A doctor

Below is a list of problems. On the lines underneath the problem, write down who would consider it a problem and who would not. Think of this in terms of who will take action because of the problem and who wouldn't do anything about it.

Example: A boy is lost in the forest.
    Problem for: The boy; the boy's parents, family and friends; and the police.
    Not a problem for: The boy's neighbors, school teacher, doctor . . .

Explanation: The boy will take actions to get un-lost. His family will take actions to find him. The boy's neighbors and teacher will certainly care and hope the boy will be found, but they will not necessarily take action to do anything about it.

1. Monkey M ate Missy Monkey's banana cream birthday cake.

    Problem for: _____

    Not a problem for: _____

2. My best friend's grandmother died.

    Problem for: _____

    Not a problem for: _____

3. A giant lobster came out of the sea and cut all the power lines in town.

    Problem for: _____

    Not a problem for: _____

4. Captain Yogger, when he was a boy, fell off his glorious elephant and broke his leg.

    Problem for: _____

    Not a problem for: _____

5. A kraken is attacking a ship full of mashed potatoes and Brintish tourists.

    Problem for: _____

    Not a problem for: _____

6. My baby brother is screaming.

    Problem for: _____

    Not a problem for: _____

7. A dragon ate all the books in the library.

    Problem for: _____

    Not a problem for: _____

8. Captain Yogger ate his last jelly bean.

    Problem for: _____

    Not a problem for: _____

9. My little sister's pollywogs were poisoned and died.

    Problem for: _____

    Not a problem for: _____

10. An asteroid is coming to destroy the earth.

    Problem for: _____

    Not a problem for: _____

What's one of your favorite stories? _____

Think of problems that occur in that story. Which character(s) take action to solve them?

Problem: _____

Character(s): _____

Problem: _____

Character(s): _____

Do this again with another story: _____

Problem: _____

Character(s): _____

Problem: _____

Character(s): _____

Problem: _____

Character(s): _____

Do this again with another story: _____

Problem: _____

Character(s): _____

Problem: _____

Character(s): _____

Problem: _____

Character(s): _____

RANKING PROBLEMS

Not all problems are created equal. In story, as in life, there are some problems that are more important than others. Problems can be ranked.

Make a list of 10 problems you face in your life right now. Then rank them as high, medium, and low priority (H / M / L).

1. _____

2. _____

3. _____

4. _____

5. _____

6. _____

7. _____

8. _____

9. _____

10. _____

ACT OF VILLAINY

Okay. It's time to pay extra close attention. What I'm going to teach you here is one of the most important things in story.

Problems are a vital element of stories, which is why – as I said earlier – stories are full of them. With so many problems, it's important for an author to know how they rank against the others. One way to do this is to identify the most important problems in a story. Because this is so significant, Captian Yogger gave them a special name. He calls the most important problem(s) in a story an Act of Villainy, or AoV for short.

An Act of Villainy is a problem that causes one or more characters to respond to try and solve it. Stories often start with an Act of Villainy and end when it is resolved.

Make your own list of problems that might happen to start a story.

1. You wake up lost in a different world.
2. You're born with stinky breath.
3. Pirate Blacknose enslaves eight monkeys.
4. _____
5. _____
6. _____
7. _____
8. _____
9. _____
10. _____

Now, take the ten Acts of Villainy you created above and think of a way they might be resolved. (Note: a single AoV can be resolved in many different ways.)

1. You never find a way home, but you come to love being a pirate and embrace your new life.
2. You find magic jelly beans that take away your stink.
3. Captain Yogger LeFossa liberates the captured monkeys.
4. _____

    _____
5. _____

    _____
6. _____

    _____

7. _____

8. _____

9. _____

10. _____

CAUSES OF AN ACT OF VILLAINY

Acts of Villainy can have many causes. Someone – possibly the Villain – intends to do harm. Or maybe someone does something that creates a problem by accident. The AoV may be caused by some act of nature. A person may cause their own Act of Villainy to happen to themselves.

CAUSED BY A VILLAIN

1. The evil _____ stole _____ from an innocent man at the bus stop.

2. Bratty Bobby built himself a giant _____ to terrorize the other kids.

3. Pollywog Pete pushed the little _____ down the _____.

4. Monkey Melody plays her _____ so loud at night because she wants to prevent Monkey Morgan from _____.

Write your own list of AoVs caused by a Villain.

1. _____

2. _____

3. _____

4. _____

5. _____

6. _____

CAUSED BY ACCIDENT

1. Alana showed up at the _____ and saw that her worst enemy was wearing the exact same dress.

2. Tom slept in until _____ and so his team lost the game.

3. A _____ ball came crashing through _____'s window.

4. Katie dropped _____ when she went down the stairs, and it _____ as it went tumbling down.

Write your own list of AoVs caused by accident.

1. _____
2. _____
3. _____
4. _____
5. _____
6. _____

CAUSED BY NATURE

1. An earthquake caused the _____ to collapse and my _____ to be crushed.

2. A fire burned down the neighbor's _____.

3. A hurricane caused the _____ to crash at Rocky Point.

4. A landslide kept the _____ hidden for decades.

Write your own list of AoVs caused by nature.

1. _____
2. _____
3. _____
4. _____
5. _____
6. _____

CAUSED BY YOURSELF

1. I never _____ for my Algebra class, and so now I have to go to summer school.

2. I ate _____ for twenty years and now I have _____.

3. I _____ my _____, and now I'm in the emergency room.

4. I told my _____ that they _____, and now they won't talk to me.

Write your own list of AoVs caused by you.

1. _____

2. _____

3. _____

4. _____

5. _____

6. _____

DESIRABLE ACTS OF VILLAINY

It's important to understand that even though we use the phrase "Act of Villainy," these problems are not always caused by an actual villain. Also, an Act of Villainy can sometimes be a desirable thing.

This is because sometimes there are "good" problems. Usually we only call something a problem when it is bad or unpleasant. But, according to the Grammar of Story, *anything* that needs to be solved is considered a problem. Imagine you always wanted to be a pirate, and one day you wake up on an actual pirate ship. This is actually a problem, because to become a true pirate you will need to take action. You are now in a different world. There will be a lot to learn, and it will take a lot of work before you can call yourself a pirate. But, because it is a problem you want to solve, we are calling it a desirable, or good, problem.

1. Norman Nopants is allowing you to make whatever you want for dinner. You're going to make

_____.

2. My step-sister got an invitation to the _____, now she needs to buy a _____.

3. Monkey M found an ultra rare _____ in his pocket and wonders who he can sell it to.

4. Mom bought a cute little _____ for your birthday!

Write your own list of non-villainous AoVs.

1. _____
2. _____
3. _____
4. _____
5. _____
6. _____

EMBRACING PROBLEMS

Most of the time we ought to avoid problems. But many people embrace problems – and Acts of Villainy – with open arms. Take our captain. The biggest fear of most captains is to encounter a kraken, but Captain LeFossa can't wait for a kraken to appear. Or, think of a doctor, a paramedic, or a lawyer. Their careers are based upon solving problems. A good doctor looks forward to the opportunity to use their skills to help a sick person be healed.

Make a list of people who have chosen to solve certain problems. Then write a description of the problem they act to resolve.

1. Doctors – solve the problem of sickness.
2. Teachers – solve the problem of ignorance.
3. Parents – guide their children into adulthood.
4. _____
5. _____
6. _____
7. _____
8. _____

There is a name for people who embrace problems and solve them: Heroes. They see a problem, consider it an Act of Villainy, and then take action to resolve it.

But what if no one cares when a problem occurs? What if someone has a big jar of jelly beans and it is stolen. If this person hates jelly beans they will probably shrug their shoulders, say "Good riddance," and forget all about it.

If no one takes action in response to a problem, then that problem was not an Act of Villainy to anyone. In such a situation nobody will do anything and therefore no story will be started. A problem only becomes an AoV if the problem is something someone wants to find a solution to.

Think of Captain LeFossa.

Circle any of the following problems you think he would take action to solve:

1. A kraken is attacking his ship.
2. He has stinky breath.
3. Norman refuses to make pizza.
4. Civilized people can't understand how he speaks.
5. He is getting a sunburn.

How about Monkey Mo Mo – which of these problems does he care enough about to take action to solve?

1. His sister is a wild monkey.
2. Captain Yogger won't let any monkey eat his jelly beans.
3. Norman refuses to make pizza.
4. Captain Yogger has stinky breath.
5. His fear of fog.

Here are some problems. Who would be a character who would take actions to solve it?

Problem: Monkeys are being made slaves. Character: _____

Problem: The coconut football team is losing. Character: _____

Problem: It's supper time and there is no supper. Character: _____

Problem: You're asleep when it's time to leave for school. Character: _____

Problem: The beach is full of trash. Character: _____

Problem: You don't understand what an Act of Villainy is. Character: _____

Think of a favorite story or movie. Can you think of a problem that one or more of the characters reacted to as an AoV? There are probably lots of them, but there usually is one big AoV that the heroic characters spend most of the story dealing with.

Story: *Star Wars: A New Hope*
AoV: Darth Vader creates the Death Star.

Story: _____
AoV: _____

_____

Story: _____
AoV: _____

_____

Now, try to imagine those stories without that AoV. What would the story be about without this AoV? Would it be largely the same or would it become something altogether different? Would it make the story boring?

Creating an AoV is a crucial step when laying the foundation of a story world.

You're sitting in class, reviewing your family tree map and wondering how they're all doing, when all of a sudden, you sense the presence of another person in the room. You turn around, ever so slowly, and see that directly behind you is Captain Yogger LeFossa – watching.

"Ahoy, matey," he flashes his golden tooth at you in the most devious of grins. You try to stay calm, but deep down, you're terrified.

"Ahoy," you reply meekly.

Captain Yogger glances around the room at all the other monkeys – who stare back at him in silence – while he very carefully pulls a bright green jelly bean from his pocket

"Jelly beans," he holds it close to his nose and inhales slowly. "Good, right?" he asks you.

Your mouth begins to water.

"Sure are."

"Well then," Captain Yogger grins and lowers it right in front of your face, "if ye think so, why don' ye go ahead, matey. Take the bean."

You hesitate. Taking a jelly bean from Captain Yogger is one of the worst things anyone can do. But, so is disobeying his orders. You chew your lower lip nervously before reluctantly taking the jelly bean into your hand.

It's warm and sticky, and has clearly been in his pocket for quite some time.

"Now," he sneers as he hobbles over to a nearby window, "throw it overboard."

At this, the monkeys hoot and holler.

"What? No . . . I can't do that." You resist because you know Captain Yogger loves eating jelly beans; you've seen him do little else since boarding this vessel.

"What's that? Ye disobeyin' an order?"

"No, no," you say as you swallow the lump that's growing in your throat.

There doesn't seem to be any other option, so with one eye closed, you nervously toss it out the window. Monkey Monica gasps, almost like she didn't expect you'd actually do it.

"Now, matey, since ye know I gots me many jelly beans, thar be little fear of me carin' or becomin' angry, aye?"

"Right." You try to sound confident, but you're shaking in your boots.

"But what if I told ye that ye just threw away me very last bean? That might be a problem fer ye, no?"

Monkey Mo Mo rises from the table and raises his hands in the air as he runs out of the room, screaming, "Dead monkeys tell no tales!"

You feel sick.

He set you up – there's no doubt about that – but why? And what are you going to do now? You just threw out Captain Yogger's last jelly bean! This is a real problem.

If they make you walk the plank, you could try to swim, but you wouldn't last long.

As you wrestle with what to do next, Captain Yogger gives you a cold stare and then drapes his grizzled arm around your shoulder.

"This is it," you think to yourself, when all of a sudden. . .

. . .he breaks out laughing!

"Yo ho ho! Ye look as white as a skeleton!"

The monkeys jump up and down and cackle with laughter as they point at you and clap their hands together.

You aren't sure what to make of this, but the joy you see in the monkeys' eyes puts you a little more at ease.

Captain Yogger pulls away from you, reaches into his pocket, and brings out a handful of colored jelly beans. He pops one in his mouth with a wry smile and hobbles to the door, chuckling to himself.

"But remember," he adds at the last second, "don't be touching me beans, unless ye be wantin' t' start a story ye not be likin' the endin' to."

Yikes! That was a close one!

What's the Act of Villainy in this story? Was it the monkeys' hooting and hollering? Captain Yogger tricking you? Was it you throwing the jelly bean away? What do you think it was?

"Ya har!" Captain Yogger pops his head back into the room and lets a big grin spread across his face. "Don't be gettin' yerself tied in brain knots, Spat! Ye created no Act o' Villainy by throwin' me bean away. I told ye t' do it! Th' real problem that ye be needin' t' solve in that example, the Act o' Villainy, was created by me!"

You stare back at him, uncertain how to respond.

"It's true," First Mate Manfred explains, "Captain Yogger created an AoV by how he entered the room. He scared you. He made you sit up and take notice. You cared about what was happening. You thought you were in trouble, and so that became an AoV for you."

"Oh," you say quietly. You aren't happy the captain caused you to be afraid on purpose in order to teach a lesson on the Grammar of Story, but at the same time, you feel relieved knowing Captain Yogger wasn't really angry with you.

"Aye, when I betook me leave from th' room, ye surely breathed a sigh o' relief, no? Me comin' in stirred ye up, but when I left, th' Act o' Villainy be liquidated – vanished, like a kraken under th' sea. Might've taken a few bits off yer life, but ye be now changed, ye be knowin' what creates an Act of Villainy."

POINT OF VIEW

Every person experiences life from their point of view. You see something one way, another person sees it a different way. I hate roller coasters. Going on one is like being tortured. (And I actually know what being tortured is like.) I stay away from them. But, you may run to them and eagerly pay a hundred banana bucks for the opportunity to ride.

When you create a story you have to understand that your characters have different points of view. They don't see things the same way. Have you ever gotten into an argument with someone?

Arguments often occur because people have different points of view. The world may look one way to you and another way to someone else.

It's not easy to see things from another person's point of view. But, as a story creator, it's an important skill to be able to step into a character's shoes and see things the way they do. This is especially true when it comes to the Act of Villainy.

Evil Pirate Blacknose captures a lovely damsel, causing Captain Yogger to battle him and rescue her. What is the AoV from the point of view of the lovely damsel and Captain Yogger?

_____

Now, imagine you are Evil Pirate Blacknose! There was probably some reason why you captured the lovely damsel. What do you think it might be?

_____

_____

This was a problem for the evil pirate, a problem that he viewed as an Act of Villainy. He took actions – capturing the lovely damsel – to solve that AoV. But, then Captain Yogger came along and messed it all up by rescuing her.

If you are Evil Pirate Blacknose, and Captain Yogger rescues the damsel you rightfully captured, you are going to see this rescue as a new Act of Villainy that you must take action in order to resolve. The evil pirate is surely going to do something to capture the damsel again!

Determine the AoV from the point of view of the characters listed:

1. Some starving monkeys break into a banana bank and steal a bunch of bananas. The police are dispatched to the scene and try to return the bananas to the vault.

    What's the AoV for the starving monkeys? _____

    What's the AoV for the police? _____

2. When Monkey Melody woke up that morning, she found she had strep throat and could hardly talk. The dance that night was cancelled, much to the dismay of the monkey mates.

    What's the AoV for Monkey Melody? _____

    What's the AoV for the monkey mates? _____

3. Marty needed to get some new glasses because he lost his when he went cliff diving off Monkey Paw Falls, but his dad was running out of money and couldn't afford to pay for them.

What's the AoV for Marty? _____

What's the AoV for his dad? _____

4. During the final FICA championships, the Southern Canmerico coconut football team was undefeated, and the Brintish had never won a championship before. Everyone thought the victory was going to go to the Southern Canmerico team, but surprisingly, the Brintish team scored several goals in the final quarter and won the game.

What's the AoV for the Brintish team? _____?

What's the AoV for the Southern Canmerico team? _____?

5. The snow storm hit the town quite unexpectedly. When everyone woke, they realized there was too much snow for anyone to get to school, so the principal declared it a snow day.

What's the AoV for the children? _____

What's the AoV for the parents? _____

What's the AoV for the city workers? _____

6. In the story of Monkeyella, the wicked stepmother forces Monkeyella to be the family servant, and refuses to let her to go to the ball. The fairy godmother comes along, works her magic, and Monkeyella gets to go. At the ball, a prince falls in love with her. When she rushes away at midnight, the prince searches to find her. When he eventually does, they get married and live happily ever after.

What's the AoV for Monkeyella? _____

What's the AoV for the prince? _____

What's the AoV for the wicked stepmother? _____

Each character has a different problem that they want to solve. Each of those problems is an AoV from that character's point of view.

"HEAVE HO!"

All right. Here's a tricky one! Using the examples we already looked at, come up with different ways for the characters in these stories to liquidate – or solve – their AoV:

1. Some starving monkeys break into a banana bank and steal a bunch of bananas. The police are dispatched to the scene and try to return the bananas to the vault.

The starving monkeys? _____

The police? _____

2. When Monkey Melody woke up that morning, she found that she had strep throat and could hardly talk. The dance that night was cancelled, much to the dismay of the monkey mates.

Monkey Melody? _____

Monkey mates? _____

3. Marty needed to get some new glasses because he lost his when he went cliff diving off Monkey Paw Falls, but his dad was running out of money and couldn't afford to pay for them.

Marty? _____

Dad? _____

4. During the final FICA championships, the Southern Canmerico coconut football team was undefeated, and the Brintish had never won a championship before. Everyone thought the victory was going to go to the Southern Canmerico team, but surprisingly, the Brintish team scored several goals in the final quarter and won the game.

The Brintish team? _____

The Southern Canmerico team? _____

5. The snow storm hit the town quite unexpectedly. When everyone woke, they realized there was too much snow for anyone to get to school, so the principal declared it a snow day.

The children? _____

The parents? _____

The city workers?_____

Take the following AoV and think of three different ways for each AoV to be liquidated.

Dragons and humans are fighting for control of an island.

1. The villagers train together and build weapons to defeat the dragons.

2. The dragons burn the humans up and take the island for themselves.

3. The humans and the dragons learn to work together.

There's only a limited amount of honey left, and Pooh Bear has company coming for dinner.

1. _____

2. _____

3. _____

Evil Pirate Blacknose needs a ship, and tries to steal ours from Captain Yogger.

1. _____

2. _____

3. _____

My grandma's dog Woof is stuck on the roof.

1. _____

2. _____

3. _____

Alien space invaders have landed in the president's backyard.

1. _____

2. _____

3. _____

A tree fell on the bike I was renting.

1. _____

2. _____

3. _____

The parents watched helplessly as their child tripped and broke her leg.

1. _____

2. _____

3. _____

A bandit stole all the jelly beans from the little girl.

1. _____

2. _____

3. _____

The town's water supply has been poisoned.

1. _____

2. _____

3. _____

My favorite teacher assigned me a super long, difficult paper.

1. _____

2. _____

3. _____

Can you see how important the Act of Villainy is?

The AoV has a huge influence on what the story is about. The AoV is what causes the characters to act. Stories often begin with an AoV and end when that AoV is resolved.

Now that we have focused on many things that build the world of the story, it's time to learn more about the characters who will take action in the story.

SCRATCH YER NOGGIN'

Choose a favorite book or movie: _____

Where does the story take place? _____

Does the story have a significant object? _____

Tell me one rule that the story world has: _____

What is the main Act of Villainy (problem) that the characters are trying to solve?

_____

_____

_____

Define:

Setting: _____

Values: _____

Significance: _____

Rules: _____

Symbols: _____

Backstory: _____

Connections: _____

Mindstorm a list of 20 food items to customize on your dream pizza:

1. _____
2. _____
3. _____
4. _____
5. _____
6. _____
7. _____
8. _____
9. _____
10. _____

11. _____
12. _____
13. _____
14. _____
15. _____
16. _____
17. _____
18. _____
19. _____
20. _____

RAISE THE ANCHOR AND SET SAIL

Time to set sail! Selecting an Act of Villainy is a great way to begin a story. What was an AoV in the exercises that stuck out to you? Use it to begin your story here:

_____

_____

_____

_____

_____

_____

_____

_____

_____

_____

_____

_____

_____

_____

_____

_____

_____

_____

_____

_____

_____

_____

_____

_____

_____

_____

_____

_____

CHAPTER AVAST AYE

You've been in class for hours, and it's nearing the end of the day. Although you find the story stuff quite interesting, your mind is beginning to wander.

All around you sit the monkey mates, heads down and scribbling frantically in monkeyscript. One of these days, you hope to actually learn that language, as you think there is something really cool about drawing pictures instead of words.

Although there are still many monkeys you don't really know, you feel pleased that you're starting to recognize certain faces and understand them better.

For example, you aren't surprised at all when you look over to your left and see Monkey Monica with her head on the table, snoozing away.

"Ahem," First Mate Manfred clears his throat. It seems he just noticed Monkey Monica as well.

When she doesn't respond, he steps over to her and taps her on the shoulder.

"I no nappin'!" she announces groggily as her head flies up. "Just thinkin' about a story."

"Uh-huh," First Mate Manfred scowls, "a story about what?"

"Well," Monkey Monica tilts her head and stares up at the ceiling, "a story about Captain Yogger, of course! And you, and me . . . on a grand adventure across the sea," she pauses, and then adds with a smile, "it's going to be a poem."

"Ha!" Missy Monkey snickers. "Nice try."

Monkey Monica sneers and sticks her tongue out at Missy Monkey, who responds with more laughter.

Through your time on the ship, you've come to see that even though Missy Monkey wears a cute, pink bow on her head, that's really the only girly thing about her. She's tough, feisty, and always ready to laugh at others' misfortune. But even though she puts up a tough front, you get the sense she does genuinely care about others.

On your right, you see Monkey Mackenzie leaning over Monkey Mo Mo's desk. Monkey Mo Mo has his hands on his face and looks really confused and upset, but Monkey Mackenzie is speaking softly and kindly to him and lending some help with the answers.

"I just want to tell a story," Monkey Mo Mo whines.

"We will, we will," Monkey Mackenzie assures, "just need to learn this first."

"This hard. I thought class be easy."

"Remember what Captain Yogger say," Monkey Mackenzie reminds, "story be hard work, but worth it."

"Yeah, yeah," Monkey Mo Mo grumbles. "But, why can't we just tell a story?"

The moment class ends, and you've been dismissed, your three roommates – Monkey Martin, Monkey Morgan, and Monkey Morta – dart out of the room and down the hall. You aren't sure where they're going, because your room is the other direction, but you aren't surprised when they sneak away; you've noticed they seem to be more mischievous than the other monkeys, and are probably up to no good.

Even though it makes you curious, you're feeling quite tired, so you turn down the hall that leads to your room.

As you go, you pass by the kitchen and spot Norman Nopants preparing some food.

"Making a late night snack?" you ask as you stop in the doorway.

"Nyet. Norman make nextfast food for morning."

"Nextfast?" you smirk. "Do you mean breakfast?"

"Nyet," Norman says without looking up. "Go to bed. Norman busy."

Even though you are really tired, you kind of would like a snack.

"Anything to eat in there? Any Nanaimo bars, or Nutella? Neapolitan ice cream?"

Norman looks up, locks eyes on you, and storms over to the door.

"Wait for morning," he growls as he shuts the door. "Night night."

You can't help but smile.

"Good-night, Norman!"

EXERCISE #11: CHARACTERIZATIONS

Characterizations describe things. These descriptions give details that define who or what a character is.

Characterizations are the bridge that connects theme and character, and are what happens when you take all you've just learned about creating an interesting story world and apply it to the characters in that world. Characterizations give us a fuller picture of who a character is.

Imagine this scene: There's a busy street corner with many horses and carriages rushing by. A little six-year-old girl and her best friend, another six-year-old, are playing near the edge of the street. An old woman is passing by them. A person with a mean-face rides through the street on a horse and tips his hat sarcastically to a strong man wearing a sheriff's hat.

This scene has five characters. I've identified each of them by describing some of their characterizations. Make a list of all five:

1. A strong man in a sheriff's hat

2. _____

3. _____

4. _____

5. _____

Now, make a list that includes yourself and four other people you know well. You will be using this list of people for many of the exercises in this lesson.

1. Yourself

2. _____

3. _____

4. _____

5. _____

PHYSICAL CHARACTER TRAITS

A simple way to characterize a character is to describe their physical traits: how someone looks (for example their height, hair color, weight, etc.).

Take the fictional characters from the scene I described and connect them with a physical characterization you want them to have.

_____ A strong man in a sheriff's hat
_____ The little girl
_____ Another six-year-old
_____ The mean-faced owner of the horse
_____ An old woman passing by

a. Is physically frail.
b. Is really short.
c. Has long legs.
d. Has long hair.
e. Has a dark complexion.

Think of 20 different kinds of physical traits (if you're stuck, think of characters you know from stories you like):

1.   Long black hair
2.   Green eyes
3.   _____
4.   _____
5.   _____
6.   _____
7.   _____
8.   _____
9.   _____
10. _____

11. _____
12. _____
13. _____
14. _____
15. _____
16. _____
17. _____
18. _____
19. _____
20. _____

List three physical characteristics each for yourself and three people you know well. Try to imagine you are seeing them for the first time. What stands out to you?

1. Yourself
    1. _____
    2. _____
    3. _____

2. _____
    1. _____
    2. _____
    3. _____

3. _____
    1. _____
    2. _____
    3. _____

4. _____
    1. _____
    2. _____
    3. _____

CHARACTER DETAILS

Characterizations can also describe details about a character. Take our fictional characters and choose some details for them by connecting each one to an option you like.

___ A strong man in a sheriff's hat   a. Jogs every morning.

___ The little girl   b. Is from a small town.

___ Another six-year-old   c. Is the owner of a ranch.

___ The mean-faced owner of the horse   d. Never learned English.

___ An old woman passing by   e. Never went to school.

List three details each about yourself and three people you know well.

1. Yourself

    1. _____

    2. _____

    3. _____

2. _____

    1. _____

    2. _____

    3. _____

3. _____

    1. _____

    2. _____

    3. _____

4. _____

    1. _____

    2. _____

    3. _____

CHARACTER ACTIVITIES

What a character does tells us about who they are, and is another kind of characterization. Once again, let's use our characters and connect them to something they do.

___ A strong man in a sheriff's hat   a. Plays a guitar.

___ The little girl   b. Never washes their clothes.

___ Another six-year-old   c. Does exercises every morning.

___ The mean-faced owner of the horse   d. Rides horses every day.

___ An old woman passing by   e. Causes mischief.

List three activities you and three people you know well are involved in.

1. Yourself

    1. _____

    2. _____

    3. _____

2. _____

    1. _____

    2. _____

    3. _____

3. _____

    1. _____

    2. _____

    3. _____

4. _____

    1. _____

    2. _____

    3. _____

CHARACTER PERSONALITY

Characterizations can include details about their personality.

Let's look at our characters. Connect the characters with something you think fits their personality.

____ A strong man in a sheriff's hat

____ The little girl

____ Another six-year-old

____ The mean-faced owner of the horse

____ An old woman passing by

a. Loves to make others laugh.

b. Avoids conflict at all costs.

c. Is easily surprised.

d. Gets angry when hungry.

e. Is compassionate with animals.

Describe three aspects of your personality and three people you know well. Think of how you would describe this person to someone who does not know them. What would you say if someone asked you what they were like?

1. Yourself

    1. _____

    2. _____

    3. _____

2. _____

    1. _____

    2. _____

    3. _____

3. _____

    1. _____

    2. _____

    3. _____

4. _____

    1. _____

    2. _____

    3. _____

SKILLS AND EXPERIENCE

Another area of characterization for a character is their skills or experience in life.

Connect the characters and the skills you choose for them.

__ A strong man in a sheriff's hat	a. Is great at braiding hair.
__ The little girl	b. Is a fast runner.
__ Another six-year-old	c. Knows how to calm an agitated horse.
__ The mean-faced owner of the horse	d. Has spent a lot of time with animals.
__ An old woman passing by	e. Is used to being in dangerous situation.

List three skills and/or experiences you and three people you know well have. To help, think of the kinds of things you would trust this person to help you with.

1. Yourself

    1. _____

    2. _____

    3. _____

2. _____

    1. _____

    2. _____

    3. _____

3. _____

    1. _____

    2. _____

    3. _____

4. _____

    1. _____

    2. _____

    3. _____

RELATIONSHIPS

Relationships can be a great source of characterizations. Who a character is to other people can tell you a lot about that character. (Think of the Grinch Who Stole Christmas; he's characterized as living away from town, alone, aside from his dog.)

Choose a relationship characterization for these characters.

__ A strong man in a sheriff's hat	a. Is a friend.
__ The little girl	b. Is a parent.
__ Another six-year-old	c. Has an uncle and aunt.
__ The mean-faced owner of the horse	d. Is single.
__ An old woman passing by	e. Has a brother and sister.

List three relationships for yourself and three people you know well. To help you, think of people who are important in your life, or the people who would be at your birthday party.

1. Yourself

    1. _____

    2. _____

    3. _____

2. _____

    1. _____

    2. _____

    3. _____

3. _____

    1. _____

    2. _____

    3. _____

4. _____

    1. _____

    2. _____

    3. _____

CLOTHING STYLE

The way a character dresses can tell you something about them. It can indicate where they are from, what they do, and even give you a glimpse of their personality.

Choose some costumes for these characters.

  ___ A strong man in a sheriff's hat

  ___ The little girl

  ___ Another six-year-old

  ___ The mean-faced owner of the horse

  ___ An old woman passing by

a. Wears overalls and dirty, brown boots.

b. Wears a grey dress with a red scarf.

c. Wears torn pants and a worn plaid shirt.

d. Dressed in fancy, big-city clothes.

e. Dressed in a uniform.

List three types/styles of clothes you and three people you know commonly wear. To help you, imagine what kinds of clothing stores you like to shop at.

1. Yourself

    1. _____

    2. _____

    3. _____

2. _____

    1. _____

    2. _____

    3. _____

3. _____

    1. _____

    2. _____

    3. _____

4. _____

    1. _____

    2. _____

    3. _____

CHARACTER VOICE

A fun type of characterization can be the specific and unique ways a character speaks. It can be their accent, the words they tend to use, the types of things they talk about, their body language, what they don't say, and many other things.

Choose the voice details that you like for these characters.

___ A strong man in a sheriff's hat	a. Says "holy shmoley" when surprised.
___ The little girl	b. Twirls hair when speaking to strangers.
___ Another six-year-old	c. Speaks in broken English.
___ The mean-faced owner of the horse	d. Lets his/her guns do the talking.
___ An old woman passing by	e. Dances to express her emotions.

List three things that are distinct about the way you and your friends communicate. It may help you to imagine that someone from another country is listening to you. What are some things about your voice or things you say that might be unique or stand out to them? What are some things you or your friends do with your hands or your body while you are talking?

1. Yourself
    1. _____
    2. _____
    3. _____
2. _____
    1. _____
    2. _____
    3. _____

3. _____
    1. _____
    2. _____
    3. _____
4. _____
    1. _____
    2. _____
    3. _____

COMPLEX CHARACTERS

Those are just a few examples of types of characterizations. There are many, many more!

When all the different types of characterizations are put together, a character becomes complex, interesting, and well-rounded. Characterization is one tool to help you make a fictional character feel like a real person.

Go back through this lesson and gather together all of the characterizations you chose for the fictional characters.

A strong man in a sheriff's hat

Character physical traits: _____

Character details: _____

Character activities: _____

Character personality: _____

Skills and experience: _____

Relationships: _____

Clothing style: _____

Character voice: _____

The little girl

Character physical traits: _____

Character details: _____

Character activities: _____

Character personality: _____

Skills and experience: _____

Relationships: _____

Clothing style: _____

Character voice: _____

Another six-year-old

Character physical traits: _____

Character details: _____

Character activities: _____

Character personality: _____

Skills and experience: _____

Relationships: _____

Clothing style: _____

Character voice: _____

The mean-faced owner of the horse

Character physical traits: _____

Character details: _____

Character activities: _____

Character personality: _____

Skills and experience: _____

Relationships: _____

Clothing style: _____

Character voice: _____

An old woman passing by

Character physical traits: _____

Character details: _____

Character activities: _____

Character personality: _____

Skills and experience: _____

Relationships: _____

Clothing style: _____

Character voice: _____

You now know a lot more about these characters. Do you see how adding characterizations helps us understand who a character is?

MAKE CHARACTERIZATIONS SPECIFIC

Do you remember our lesson at the beginning about being specific? Characterizations, like all things in story, are something you should strive to be as specific with as possible.

Take a characterization such as "loves school." This tells us something about a character, but look what happens when I describe this character with more specific characterizations.

- Goes to school

- Is a student

- Spends six hours a day on homework

- His best friend is a teacher

- Thinks about school when driving to work

- Dreams about going to school full time

- Is 35 years old

Doesn't this more specific list of characterizations give you a much better picture of someone who loves school? Did you expect this character to be an adult? Does knowing they are 35 years old change your sense of what "his best friend is a teacher" looks like?

See if you can get more specific with these characterizations:

Characterization: Sleepy

1. _____
2. _____
3. _____
4. _____
5. _____

Characterization: Drinks hot liquids

1. _____
2. _____
3. _____
4. _____
5. _____

Characterization: Is a parent

1. _____
2. _____
3. _____
4. _____
5. _____

Characterization: Hates teeth

1. _____
2. _____
3. _____
4. _____
5. _____

Characterization: Dances

1. _____
2. _____
3. _____
4. _____
5. _____

Characterization: Loves the color orange

1. _____
2. _____
3. _____
4. _____
5. _____

Take yourself, and one of the characterizations you wrote about yourself, and make it more specific so it will communicate a more detailed picture of who you are.

Your characterization: _____

1. _____
2. _____
3. _____
4. _____
5. _____

Now do the same thing with one of the characterizations you gave to someone you know.

_____'s characterization: _____

1. _____
2. _____
3. _____
4. _____
5. _____

_____'s characterization: _____

1. _____
2. _____
3. _____
4. _____
5. _____

_____'s characterization: _____

1. _____
2. _____
3. _____
4. _____
5. _____

CHAPTER AVAST AYE AYE

"No way!"

"Aye. At last. . ."

"We cut it?"

"Yeah! Cut! Cut!"

"Quiet!"

The hushed voices of your monkey roommates wake you.

You roll over and notice they're all out of their beds and sitting cross-legged in the middle of the room.

"LeFossa, LeFossa, da big pirate bossa," one of the monkeys – Monkey Morgan, you think – sings the captain's name mischievously.

"What are you guys. . ." you start to say, when all of a sudden, you notice that the bright green jelly bean Captain Yogger made you throw out the window is right there in the middle of the room!

"Hey! That's th–" Before you can finish your sentence, Monkey Martin leaps into your bunk, wraps a dirty hand around your mouth, and presses a cold knife against your throat.

"Nice 'n easy, Spat," the voice of Monkey Martin hisses in your ear, "ye don't want t' be botherin' anyone by making a commotion now, do ye?"

"No," your voice is muffled as you speak through his furry hand.

Monkey Martin slowly lowers his hand.

"We been waitin' fer a long time t' get our paws on one o' LeFossa's beans. An' ye just tossed it away like a fool."

"How do you have it now?" you ask as you watch the other two monkeys cut it up into three even pieces.

"We has our ways, Spat."

Monkey Martin slips away from you and back down to join the others.

As soon as the jelly bean is divided into three, each of the monkeys takes their piece and places it into their mouth.

Even though you know it was wrong for them to steal that jelly bean, part of you wishes they cut a piece of it for you, too.

"It is delicious! I . . . I think," Monkey Martin looks confused.

"Aye!" Monkey Morgan nods. "Kind of . . . strange texture."

"Chewy, not like jelly at all."

"More like . . . sweet, then savory, ya know?" Monkey Morta says.

"Not salty at all."

From the way they are speaking, you wonder if they've ever eaten a jelly bean before.

The three monkeys sit and debate amongst themselves for a few minutes as to whether or not they like the bean, before finally coming to the consensus that they love it.

"We must have more!" Monkey Morgan cries.

"More! More!" Monkey Morta says.

"Aye. We will. Just keep t' the plan, mates," Monkey Martin glances back up at you and waves the knife around. "As fer ye – Ye best be keepin' this to yerself. If ye want t' live, that is."

You swallow nervously.

"Keep what to myself? I forgot already," you reply weakly.

The monkeys look confused for a moment. Then it dawns on them that you're only playing dumb. They smile and chuckle to themselves.

"Good. Sleep now, baby child. This all be just a dream."

You are really tired, and do genuinely want to fall asleep, but tonight it seems the monkeys are gassier than normal, and the room is soon so unbearably stinky that you're forced to take your pillow and blanket and sleep in the hall.

Much to the dismay of you and the rest of the crew, those three monkeys remain extra gassy. The smell is putrid, kind of like milk that's gone bad. No one seems to understand why, and so First Mate Manfred orders them to remain up on deck, in the fresh air, until they get their gas under control.

That night, you sleep alone in your room, and it's the first night you've been here that you have a peaceful, smell-free sleep.

EXERCISE #12: CHARACTERIZATIONS, PART TWO

When you know someone well, you can describe them. You've spent time watching and talking with them. You know what they like and don't like. If you want to know them better, you can go do something together and find out more. But when you are a writer, *you* have to create the character; you can't go talk to your fictional character and ask them questions like you can a living person. So how does a writer do it?

The process of creating a character is called Character Design.

Characters exist in a world. They live in a specific setting, go to events, have values, follow rules, exist in a web of connections, have a backstory and face all manner of problems. This is why we focused on world-building first. Once you know your story world, you will know what kinds of characters exist in that world. You are on our pirate ship, which is a specific setting. It's a pirate world. So what kinds of characters would you expect in a world full of pirates? (You're allowed to look back at the story for the following exercises if you need a reminder.)

Describe six characterizations of Captain Yogger LeFossa:

1. Two peg legs
2. _____
3. _____

4. _____
5. _____
6. _____

This world also has a specific kind of worldling: talking monkeys. It's a talking-monkey world. So, take a look around the ship at all the monkey mates. They each have their own distinct characterizations. Choose one, and describe five things you know about their characterizations:

Norman Nopants

1. Wears no pants
2. Has a Russkan accent
3. Is the cook of the ship
4. Says "Nyet" instead of "No"
5. Cooks only things with "N" names

Monkey _____

1. _____
2. _____
3. _____
4. _____
5. _____

Talking monkeys and pirate captains may be strange to you, but we can't imagine anything else because this is our world and our home. You, Scurvy Spat, are actually a very strange character to us. Just like you've had to get to know us, we need to get to know you. So, write down six characterizations that describe you. Remember, be specific and use as much detail as possible:

1. _____
2. _____
3. _____

4. _____
5. _____
6. _____

CHARACTER SPECIFICS

Let me tell you about a character: "There was a man. He was ugly and bad."

Do these words tell you much about this character? Do they make you want to know more about him? Not likely. So, what can we do? Let's be more specific and concrete and see if we can bring this character to life:

-Man

-A short man

-A short man with curly hair and a long red beard

-A short man with curly hair and a long red beard, who carries a monkey on his shoulder

-A short man with curly hair and a long red beard, who carries a monkey on his shoulder, and limps because his ankle was broken as a small child

-A short man with curly hair and a long red beard, who carries a monkey on his shoulder, and limps because his ankle was broken as a small child, who never smiles but when he's happy, he mutters a loud, "humph!"

Slowly, step-by-step, we added details until we have an image of Captain Yogger's old nemesis, Ol' Stumpy Humph (aka Captain Redbeard). You can refer back to the work you did in Exercise 11 for ideas.

1. Choose one and circle: a man, woman, girl, boy

Now, add a characterization: _____

Add another characterization: _____

Add another characterization: _____

Add another characterization: _____

Add another characterization: _____

Let's do another one, but make it totally different from the first.

2. Choose and circle the same word as before: a man, woman, girl, boy

Now, add a characterization: _____

Add another characterization: _____

Add another characterization: _____

Add another characterization: _____

Add another characterization: _____

Now you have two characters with details that you can see and, hopefully, feel.

Let's go back to Captain Yogger's nemesis, Ol' Stumpy Humph. I also described him as *"ugly and bad."* I want you to make each of these words more specific by adding five characterizations. As you do, remember, he's a pirate captain living in a pirate world.

Starting word: Ugly

1. _____
2. _____
3. _____
4. _____
5. _____

Starting word: Bad

1. _____
2. _____
3. _____
4. _____
5. _____

CHARACTER NAME

One of the most important aspects of creating a character is coming up with their name.

Mindstorm 20 names: 10 boy names and 10 girl names.

1. _____
2. _____
3. _____
4. _____
5. _____
6. _____
7. _____
8. _____
9. _____
10. _____

1. _____
2. _____
3. _____
4. _____
5. _____
6. _____
7. _____
8. _____
9. _____
10. _____

Sometimes a storyteller will choose the first name that drops out of their mind for a character. Other times they will work long and hard to find a name they think is right.

One tool to create names (usually last names) is to combine two words together. This is the same thing we did earlier when we created new words in our lesson on symbolism.

Think of twenty words:

1. Wood
2. Hair
3. Water
4. _____
5. _____
6. _____
7. _____
8. _____
9. _____
10. _____

11. _____
12. _____
13. _____
14. _____
15. _____
16. _____
17. _____
18. _____
19. _____
20. _____

Now, combine two of these words to create a last name. For fun, you can add a first name that starts with the first letter of the last name.

1. Warren Woodwater
2. Woody Waterhair
3. _____
4. _____
5. _____
6. _____

7. _____
8. _____
9. _____
10. _____
11. _____
12. _____

Another tool to help build names is to consider your story world.

Choose one of the following thematic worlds:

Medieval times / The distant future / Outer space / Your grandparents' days / The animal kingdom / Under the sea / Sports / Video games / Princesses / Fairy tales

Mindstorm 20 words that might belong in this world. For example, for Medieval times: sword, knight, Arthur or quest. For Under the sea: water, kelp, bubble or shark.

1. _____
2. _____
3. _____
4. _____
5. _____
6. _____
7. _____
8. _____
9. _____
10. _____

11. _____
12. _____
13. _____
14. _____
15. _____
16. _____
17. _____
18. _____
19. _____
20. _____

Now take your list of words and mindstorm 10 names that might belong in this world. For example, for Medieval times: Arthur Stonesword or Anna Knightsbane. For Under the sea: Julie Waterkelp or Marty Bubbleman.

1. _____
2. _____
3. _____
4. _____
5. _____
6. _____

7. _____
8. _____
9. _____
10. _____
11. _____
12. _____

A character's name can make a big impact on how that character is viewed. For example, Allen Smith is kind of a normal-sounding name. But if you make it Allen Lockwill, you suddenly get the sense that this is one intense and stubborn man (he's "all in" and his "will" is "locked".) Or, if you called him Allen Almost, you get the sense that he is clumsy or one step behind everyone.

Thus, in addition to inventing great names by combing two words together (lock + will), you can think of a cool, interesting, evocative, or funny sounding word.

Give the following characters new last names based on the theme.

1. David:

Comedy: David Dunderly

Horror: David Dread

Romance: David Rosered

Action: Danger Dave

3. Stephen

Comedy: _____

Horror: _____

Romance: _____

Action: _____

2. Sally

Comedy: _____

Horror: _____

Romance: _____

Action: _____

4. _____

Comedy: _____

Horror: _____

Romance: _____

Action: _____

Names are great ways to paint an image of a character in your mind. The name you give a character can communicate a lot about them, such as where they're from, their family background, and even the type of story they belong in.

Compare the following lists:

GROUP A:
Lionel Richardson the Third
Stephen Hilbert
Jessica Goldsworth
Michelle Gunderson
Hunter S. Foswell

GROUP B:
C.R. Steele
Stanley Stone
Jamie Jones
Molly Maxwell
Peter Parks

GROUP C:
Silver Star
Lori Laura Lexington
Katie Cross
Michael Knight
Jericho James

GROUP D:
Dudley Drip
Nora Nostril
Hippie Hops
Denny Doe
Billy Broom

Which column sounds more like they could be secret agents? _____

Which column sounds more like they could be movie stars? _____

Which column sounds more like they could be from rich families? _____

Which column sounds more like they belong in a comedy? _____

When you hear the name "Lionel Richardson the Third," you likely assume he comes from wealth or a very formal family. Likewise, when you hear the name "Hippy Hop," you expect the character will be silly.

Come up with your own names for these categories. Don't stress over this. Have fun!

1. Secret agents:

_____

_____

_____

2. Movie stars:

_____

_____

_____

3. Comes from a rich, formal family:

_____

_____

_____

4. Comedic names:

_____

_____

_____

5. Heroic names:

_____

_____

_____

6. Villainous names:

_____

_____

_____

7. Fantasy names:

_____

_____

_____

8. Alien names:

_____

_____

_____

9: Old people names:

_____

_____

_____

10. _____ names:

_____

_____

_____

CREATING A CHARACTER

Now, you are going to create some characters.

First, choose a thematic world this character lives in.

Medieval times / The distant future / Outer space / Your grandparents' days / The animal kingdom /
Under the sea / Sports / Video games / Princesses / Fairy tales

Next, give your character three physical
characterizations:

_____

_____

_____

Give three relational characterizations:

_____

_____

_____

Give three behavioral/personality traits:

_____

_____

_____

Give three clothing descriptions:

_____

_____

_____

Give three skills or experiences:

_____

_____

_____

Give three vocal characterizations:

_____

_____

_____

Give your character three background details.

_____

_____

_____

Now, look back at all of the characterizations you've given this character and use them to help you come up with a name for this character:_____

You've just created a character! You probably don't know what they want yet, but I bet you have a good picture of who they are.

Write a few sentences describing this character using those characterizations.

_____

_____

_____

_____

_____

Let's do it again. This time, create a character who would be an enemy/rival to the character you just created.

Give three physical characterizations:

_____

_____

_____

Give three behavioral/personality traits:

_____

_____

_____

Give three skills or experiences:

_____

_____

_____

Give three relational characterizations:

_____

_____

_____

Give three clothing descriptions:

_____

_____

_____

Give three vocal characterizations:

_____

_____

_____

Give your character three background details.

_____

_____

_____

Now, look back at all of the characterizations you've given this character and use them to help you come up with a name for this character:_____

Write a few sentences describing this character using those characterizations.

_____

_____

_____

_____

_____

CHAPTER AVAST AYE AYE AYE

You wake up the next morning to loud noises above you.

You wipe the sleep out of your eyes and stumble out of bed. You look into the other rooms. Every one is empty. You aren't sure where the other monkeys are, but you bet it means trouble.

Stepping out onto the deck, you see them; a crowd of monkeys have gathered around what appears to be a giant crate filled to the brim with bananas.

"That's weird," you say to yourself as you struggle to make sense of what you're seeing.

It's then that you notice Norman leaning casually against the wall and decide to ask him what's happening.

He spits as soon as you do.

"Banana on board."

"Banana on board?" you repeat. "What's that mean?"

"They caught for have bananas."

You wrinkle your nose.

"I thought you guys weren't allowed to eat bananas?"

"Exactly."

You bite your lower lip in frustration. It seems once again Norman prefers to be more cryptic then helpful.

"Avast, ye lard-kissing, lice-licking, limey pig-swine!" Captain Yogger shouts. "Ye were told no bananas, yet I find ye hidden stash. Plundered from th' Brintish ship, I reckon. Tell me, why do I say no bananas on board, aye?"

Norman spits and leaves the area.

"Because banana make us smell bad," Monkey Maxine responds proudly.

"Aye, thay do," Captain Yogger agrees. "So, why th' secret stash? Do ye value a nice, yell'o banana more than yer capt'n?"

"No way!" Monkey Maxine exclaims.

"Ye think so? Show me. Grab a banana. Each of ye."

It doesn't make much sense to you, but the monkeys all reach into the crate, pull out a banana, and hold it. They don't peel it or eat it or do anything other than hold it – some tightly in both hands while others, like Monkey Martin, lean their heads back and drape it over their nose in an attempt to look cool or casual.

Ten minutes go by, and most of the monkeys seem to have no problem hanging on to the banana. But, you notice a few tremble and shake.

Sweat breaks out across the forehead of Monkey Maxine. She appears to be struggling the most.

"I . . . can't . . ." she whines, and – all at once – she lets out a howl.

It's echoed by six other moneys, who are also unable to resist. The next thing you know, they tear the peel off the banana. It takes them less than a second to stuff the entire thing into their mouths, and the immediate result is a look of pure joy. They spin and dance and clap their hands, before falling on their backs and giggling.

The other monkeys seem to have more self-control, and keep their eyes locked straight ahead. They haven't wavered, moved, or made a single sound.

"All right. Put 'em back," Captain Yogger sneers after a few more minutes pass.

And just like that, the monkeys who still have bananas throw them into the crate as if they were poisonous. Two of them grab the lid, seal the crate, and drag it to the side of the ship.

Meanwhile, the monkeys who succumbed to their cravings have lost the delight of their snack and shamefully toss the peels into the ocean.

The captain doesn't say anything – not right away, at least. He just hobbles over to them and places his arms behind his back.

After a long and drawn out silence, Monkey Maxine burps. "'Scuse me." She blushes.

At that moment, one of the most foul, mind-numbingly disgusting smells oozes out of them and nearly knocks you over. In this moment, you wish you had no sense of smell.

"Feelin' mighty good, are ye? Bellies nice and happy?"

"B-b-but . . . y-y-ou no understand. W-w-we could no help it," one stammers.

"Oh, but me thinks ye can," Captain Yogger says. "Ye don't care about yer smell?" "No, no." The monkeys shake their head in protest. "We care!"

You wonder if anyone could like that smell. The closest thing you can think of to describe it is what you image a rotting piece of meat would smell like when sitting out in the hot sun after being vomited out of a cat.

"Me thinks ye like it–"

"We don't like it," they interrupt.

"Me thinks ye like it more than ye be likin' no eatin' bananas," Yogger finishes.

The seven who ate bananas lower their heads.

"I warned ye many a time. We almost be t' our destination. Now, if ye be still wantin' bananas, ye clearly ain't valuin' th' treasure."

"We do!" Monkey Maxine protests, but then spots a piece of banana stuck to her arm hair and immediately pulls it off and eats it.

"Nar, nar," Captain Yogger sighs, "ye don't."

*   *   *

Later that day you stand on the deck and watch as the seven monkeys who disobeyed Captain Yogger leave the ship and go onto on an island with the crate full of bananas. The only one of that group you talked with much was Monkey Maxine. A part of you is sad to see her go.

"Ye have one last chance," Captain Yogger LeFossa shouts from the ship to the monkeys who are now on shore. "Do ye want yer bananas, or do ye want to go with me?"

The monkeys are clearly struggling with the decision. They look from one to the other and examine the island and the crate. Some go so far as to even chew on their own tails!

"Wait!" Four of the seven monkeys take apprehensive steps forward. "We want to change! We no want to value bananas! We promised we eat no bananas. Forgive us!" they cry.

You look to Captain Yogger to see what he will do, and are relieved when you see him nod to them and say, "Ye may come back."

The four swim as hard and as fast as they can until they are back on the ship.

"Thank you!" they cry, bowing their heads repeatedly.

"Aye, ye smell worse than me breath on me birthday! Upper deck duty until ye lose that thar banana stink." The monkeys clap their hands and scamper away.

But, even though four returned, three chose to stay.

146

You look back at the newly marooned monkeys – Monkey Maxine especially. She doesn't look remorseful; her face is full and stuffed with bananas, and she waves happily as you set back out to sea.

At least he gave them the bananas, you think to yourself, until you notice that the island he dropped them at is full of banana trees.

"Oh wow. They'll definitely have their fill of bananas now!" you say out loud. "That's really not such a bad deal for them, I guess."

Mini Mate overhears you, and slaps the front of his own face.

"Ye kiddin'? They no be gettin' treasure now!" he exclaims as he hobbles away in an imitation of Captain Yogger's walk. You notice he recently attached wooden planks to his legs in order to make his walk more stilted.

"But they get bananas..."

"Exactly, Spat," Captain Yogger's voice startles you, "they be gettin' what they value most."

You nod, but don't make eye contact. Even though you know this pirate was once a peaceful prince, there's still something incredibly terrifying about him.

"Aye, aye," you meekly reply.

Captain Yogger grunts and starts to wander away. But before he gets too far, he stops and glances over his shoulder.

"What ye be valuin', Spat?"

Before you can figure out an answer, he disappears into the depths of the ship and leaves you to stew on your thoughts.

EXERCISE #13: CHARACTER VALUES

As we discussed before, values are things that are valuable. But now, we're going to be looking at the values of the characters in your story.

Character values reflect what a particular character believes to be important, worthwhile or useful in a story. In other words: _Character values are the things that are valuable to characters._

Circle all of the following that you personally value:

Math	Salad	Cooking	Bananas
Sports	Poems	Board games	Justice
Writing	Friends	Ping pong	Exercise
Music	Family	Watching TV	Dirt
Reading	Sailing	Photography	Sea horses
Movies	Fluffy animals	Travelling	Money
Swabbing decks	Coconut football	Fashion	Building stuff
Being fast	Hamburgers	Dish washing	Jelly beans
Being accurate	Pizza	Cars	Computers
Winning	Pumpkin soup	Education	Saving monkeys
Books	Video games	Religion	Ice cream
Riding kraken	Soccer	Nature	
Sword fighting	Dolls	Learning	

There are no right or wrong answers here; everything you circled above is something you value.

Now list three of the items from the above list that you did not circle:

1._____ 2._____ 3. _____

Imagine a character who would have these three things as values.

Give him/her a name: _____ Describe him/her:_____

_____

_____

Do it again. List three of the items from the above list that you did not circle:

1._____ 2._____ 3. _____

Imagine a character who would have these three things as values.

Give him/her a name: _____ Describe him/her:_____

_____

_____

One more. List three of the items from the above list that you did not circle:

1._____ 2._____ 3. _____

Imagine a character who would have these three things as values.

Give him/her a name: _____ Describe him/her:_____

_____

_____

CHOICES

Often, it's hard to know what people really value. One way authors reveal the values of their characters is to put them in situations where they have to make choices. This works well because our choices reveal our values!

Imagine the Evil Pirate Hargoon Smackface is attacking your home town! Fire has spread through your neighborhood. You have to leave. Now! You frantically try to save whatever you can before Hargoon and his ship full of mean-spirited Munchyurian Capuchins start to loot the city! You only have enough room in your backpack for four things – what will you bring?

1. _____

2. _____

3. _____

4. _____

This situation forced you to chose the things you value most. Someone else – your father or sister – might choose different objects. This is because different people have different values.

USEFULNESS

Some things are valuable to someone based on that person's personal opinion. Other objects are valuable because of their *usefulness* to a character. Coconuts are valuable if you are playing coconut football.

List four things that are valuable to the following characters because they are useful.

Someone working in a jelly bean factory:

1. _____
2. _____
3. _____
4. _____

A circus clown:

1. _____
2. _____
3. _____
4. _____

A student taking a test:

1. _____
2. _____
3. _____
4. _____

A little spider monkey locked in a cage:

1. _____
2. _____
3. _____
4. _____

An author writing a story:

1. _____
2. _____
3. _____
4. _____

An evil slaver hunting for monkeys:

1. _____
2. _____
3. _____
4. _____

A pirate marooned on a desert island:

1. _____
2. _____
3. _____
4. _____

A dentist about to work on some teeth:

1. _____
2. _____
3. _____
4. _____

VALUES LEAD TO ACTIONS

Just like we saw in the cultural values section, when a person values something, you will find evidence of that in what they do. For example, someone who places a high value on "law and order" may become a police officer, a judge, or a lawyer; they will obey laws and may work to make sure other people obey laws too.

Below, there is a list of values. Find a good job for a person who holds this value.

1. Value: Law and order   Job: Judge
2. Value: Cooking   Job: Chef
3. Value: Emotional health Job: Counselor
4. Value: Beauty   Job: _____
5. Value: Stories   Job: _____
6. Value: Safety   Job: _____
7. Value: Money   Job: _____
8. Value: Fame   Job: _____
9. Value: God   Job: _____
10. Value: Helping the poor Job: _____

A person's values will lead them to take all kinds of different actions.

If someone values <u>bananas</u>, what are some things they might want to do?

1. Move to Banana Island
2. Bake banana biscuits
3. Put up banana wallpaper on their walls
4. Grow banana trees in their back yard

If a character in your story values <u>adventure</u>, what are some things they might do?

1. _____   3. _____
2. _____   4. _____

If a 90-year-old woman in your story values <u>family</u>, what are some things she might do?

1. _____   3. _____
2. _____   4. _____

If Evil Pirate Hargoon Smackface in your story values <u>revenge</u>, what are some things he might do?

1. _____   3. _____
2. _____   4. _____

If a kidnapped monkey in your story values <u>freedom</u>, what are some things they might do?

1. _____   3. _____
2. _____   4. _____

If a violent kraken, Kelly, in your story values <u>eating ships</u>, what are some things she might do?

1. _____   3. _____
2. _____   4. _____

MORALS

Characters also hold specific moral values. Like all values, moral values affect what a character believes and does. They are also a major factor in whether or not a character is considered "good" or "evil."

List four moral values for a Hero and four moral values for a Villain: (Remember moral values are things like honesty, hard-work, integrity.)

Hero

1. _____
2. _____
3. _____
4. _____

Villain

1. _____
2. _____
3. _____
4. _____

OPPOSING VALUES

Some values stand in opposition to another value. (This is often true of moral values.) Take honesty, for example, which is in opposition to lying. We don't often think of lying as something valuable, but it sure is to someone who believes they can get something they want by lying.

The ability to steal something is a valuable skill for a thief. Imagine Evil Pirate Hargoon Smackface. He has a different set of moral values, based on what is valuable to *him*. Lying, cheating, and stealing may not be "right" and "good" from his point of view, but they are valuable. Why? Because they help him accomplish what he wants, which is to plunder.

Create some pairs of opposing values.

1. Honesty vs. lying
2. Generosity vs. stinginess
3. _____

4. _____
5. _____
6. _____

CONFLICT

Opposing values are a crucial element in story. This is because they create conflict and conflict is essential for a story. If all the characters in your story hold the same values, what is the story going to be about? If there are no problems, there will be no Acts of Villainy, and thus no story.

Imagine a story world where everyone values chocolate. Everyone loves it, no one is allergic to it, and every factory makes so much of it the streets are paved with it. What a delightful world! But, as delicious as it may be, if you wrote a story about this place, it would be the most boring story ever written. This is because everyone has the same values.

So, what can a writer do? They can create a character that has an opposing value. We will call this person the Chocolate Nazi because they believe chocolate is unhealthy, fattening, selfish, and altogether evil. They want to tear down the chocolate factories and grow Brussels sprouts on the land. They are the kind of person who hands out toothbrushes on Halloween. Wicked, wicked villain.

Come up with your own characters based on these opposing values.

1. If a <u>police officer</u> values the law, they would have conflict with a <u>thief</u>, who values stealing.

2. If a _____ values healing, they would have conflict with a _____, who values killing.

3. If a _____ values telling the truth, they would have conflict with a _____, who values lying.

4. If a _____ values sharing knowledge, they would have conflict with _____, who values secrecy.

5. If a _____ values loud music, they would have conflict with a _____, who values peace and quiet.

Now come up with your own characters and values.

1. If a _____ values _____, they would have conflict with a _____, who values _____.

2. If a _____ values _____, they would have conflict with a _____, who values _____.

3. If a _____ values _____, they would have conflict with a _____, who values _____.

4. If a _____ values _____, they would have conflict with a _____, who values _____.

As a story creator, you need to create characters that have values – especially moral values – that are different from your own. Understanding opposing values can help you with this.

A PLETHORA OF VALUES

Not all conflict in stories comes from opposing values that are total opposites. Most conflict in story, as well as in life, comes from less obvious differences.

Consider the value of "hard work." This means different things to different people. Write down a variety of ways different characters may demonstrate they value "hard work." I'll start it off.

1. Someone who always goes above and beyond what's required of them
2. A character who only works hard when their boss is looking
3. A person who works as hard as they are expected to, but no more
4. _____
5. _____
6. _____
7. _____

How about the value of "generosity"?

1. Someone who gives generously to members of their family but is stingy with everyone else
2. A person who is generous with their time but not their money.
3. Someone who gives the appearance of being generous but who, in fact, isn't
4. _____
5. _____
6. _____
7. _____

Stories are more interesting when they contain characters who are different from one another. Giving your characters different perspectives on the same value is one way to do this.

When your characters have strong unique values, conflict ensues. And where there is conflict, there's a story!

154

"HEAVE HO!"

Here is a list of moral values:

Honesty / Generosity / Patience / Cooperativeness / Kindness / Self-control / Justice / Empathy

Compassion / Respectfulness / Forgiveness / Friendship / Open-mindedness

Choose One: _____

Describe how you think Monkey Monica views this value.

_____

_____

How about Mini Mate?

_____

_____

What about Monkey Martin? He's the grumpiest Monkey in the crew!

_____

_____

Choose another moral value from above: _____

Once again, describe how each of the following monkeys views it.

Monkey Martin:

_____

_____

Mini Mate:

_____

_____

Monkey Monica:

_____

_____

Write down the name of a favorite fictional character. Choose one who you continue to remember and think about long after you've finished the story they are in.

        Name: _____

In the space below, write down this character's values. Think of as many things as you can remember.

Now, circle the ones you think this character values the most.

Think of another character and do the same thing. Name: _____

Values:

Circle the ones you think this character values the most.

EXERCISE #14: THE LINE BETWEEN LIGHT AND DARK

Another way to characterize the characters in your story is based on where they stand in relation to the Act of Villainy (AoV). *For all characters, the AoV becomes a dividing line that separates them into two different sides.*

One group of characters will consider the Act of Villainy a problem that needs to be liquidated (resolved). We will describe characters like this as standing on the side of Light.

Another set of characters will consider the Act of Villainy a good thing, and so the AoV will be something they promote and support. We will describe characters like this as standing on the side of Dark.

1. Act of Villainy: The ruthless Pirate Orangebeard captures the Monkey Monarch's daughter.

Which character(s) views the AoV as a problem? (Light) _____

Which character(s) considers the AoV as a good thing? (Dark) _____

2. Act of Villainy: A small farming village is under constant attack by bandits, who come every harvest and steal their grain.

Which character(s) views the AoV as a problem? (Light) _____

Which character(s) considers the AoV as a good thing? (Dark) _____

3. Act of Villainy: A girl who loves bugs is taught by her parents that bugs are not safe and should be killed on sight.

Which character(s) views the AoV as a problem? (Light) _____

Which character(s) considers the AoV as a good thing? (Dark) _____

4. Act of Villainy: Monkey Martin was orphaned when his parents sold him as a slave for a bundle of bananas.

Which character(s) views the AoV as a problem? (Light) _____

Which character(s) considers the AoV as a good thing? (Dark) _____

5. Act of Villainy: Captain Yogger – when he was younger and more proud – tried to defeat Class 5 Kraken Kenny on his own. He failed, and lost his legs as a result.

Which character(s) views the AoV as a problem? (Light) _____

Which character(s) considers the AoV as a good thing? (Dark) _____

Some stories, like the ones above, will have good, right characters on the Light side and bad, evil characters on the Dark side. But, it's a character's perspective on the AoV that determines if they are on the Light or Dark side, not if they are good or evil.

The dividing line is the character's point of view in regard to the Act of Villainy.

Let me tell you a story:

> About a year ago, we were resting at Port Golden Beauty, when we ran into one of Captain Yogger's old foes, the Dread Pirate Plaquebeard – a man whose smell was worse than any monkey I've ever met. Plaquebeard owed Captain Yogger a lot of money, but he said he couldn't pay it back. He did, however, have a map leading to some ancient treasure on the Island of Nickel and Scents. If Yogger forgave the debt, Plaquebeard would share the treasure.
>
> Captain Yogger and us monkey mates made a tentative alliance with Plaquebeard and his crew of ornery orangutans, and all set sail together.
>
> With our combined effort, it didn't take long at all to find the Island of Nickel and Scents, and we were soon out exploring it and all its strange, exotic creatures. Everything smelt so good there, and we started to think this place might have nothing but good smells. That was, until Monkey Marco (the monkey you know today as Mini Mate) was dared by Orangutan Ollie and Orangutan Omar to pick up a blue cat that was wandering by.
>
> Turns out the cat was a skunk, and it sprayed him with some awful, blue-colored nastiness that made him stink worse than anything we could ever have imagined. When it happened, Missy Monkey couldn't stop laughing.
>
> Our adventure was excruciatingly painful after that, as the only thing any of us could smell was Marco. Missy Monkey didn't think it was funny anymore and kept on saying, "someone needs to find a way to get rid of his stink."
>
> "It true. We can no be goin' on like this!" Plaquebeard also grumbled.
>
> "What's wrong?" Captain Yogger growled. "He be smellin' no worse than ye and yer nasty beard! We can deal wit' th' smell after we get th' treasure."
>
> "No, no, he do smell worse. Far worse," Plaquebeard sneered, "look how miserable he be!"
>
> Sure enough, Monkey Marco looked very discouraged.
>
> "I feel awful," he sighed.
>
> "Aw, poor lil' monkey," Plaquebeard cooed. "I think I be havin' me an idea. . ."
>
> And so, after an argument between the two captains, the expedition agreed to stop. Captain Yogger didn't want to detour from the mission, but Monkey Marco begged him to let Plaquebeard try his idea. And so, we returned to our ships, where Plaquebeard had Orangutan Ollie and Omar collect all their stored milk. They took it all to a hot spring on the island and poured the milk into the water and had Mini Mate take a long bath. Captain Yogger and I were skeptical of any good coming from Plaquebeard, but it turned out that he was right. Before long, Monkey Marco's blue-stained fur started to return to its normal color. After some scrubbing, Monkey Marco was rid of that smell.
>
> "I told ye!" Plaquebeard cried. "C'mon! Let's all swim!"
>
> Plaquebeard tucked his knees into his chest and did a cannon ball into the water, creating such a splash that the rest of us couldn't help but get wet. But, it looked like so much fun, none of us cared, and soon we all were bathing in the milky water.

This is an example of how a villainous character can be on the side of Light (if only for a specific AoV).

What is the Act of Villainy for Monkey Marco in this story?_____

Which characters are proponents of the AoV? (Dark)

_____

Which characters view the AoV as a problem? (Light)

_____

Unfortunately for Captain Yogger, Plaquebeard orchestrated this situation to advance his evil plan. While he was on the side of light for Monkey Marco's AoV – he really had compassion for Monkey Marco – he was still on the side of Dark for the larger AoV of the larger story.

While we were so busy bathing and having fun in the pool of milk, Plaquebeard commanded Orangutan Ollie and Orangutan Omar to sneak away and steal the treasure. By the time we realized what had happened, Plaquebeard and his ornery Orangutans were long gone, and their debt remained unpaid.

From Captain Yogger's perspective, the Act of Villainy wasn't resolved, and so the story isn't finished yet.

After that, Monkey Marco adopted the name Mini Mate, pledged his loyalty to Captain Yogger, and is committed to fight Plaquebeard given the opportunity.

What is the Act of Villainy for the larger story from the point of view of Captain Yogger?

_____

Which characters are proponents of the AoV? (Dark)

_____

Which characters view the AoV as a problem? (Light)

_____

Here is another AoV: The deans of the high school decide dancing won't be allowed at this year's annual "welcome-back-to-school" party.

From the following list of characters, determine who could be a Light character and a Dark character for this AoV. (Write "Light" or "Dark" on the line.)

The chaperones who feel bad for the kids. _____

The principal who doesn't like dancing. _____

The cool kid who hates dances. _____

The shy boy who never learned to dance. _____

The adventurous girl who loves to dance. _____

The girl who loves to dance, but who agrees with the decision. _____

The boy and girl who want to have their first dance. _____

Create characters who would fall on the Light and Dark sides of the following Acts of Villainy.

AoV: It hasn't stopped snowing for a week.

     Light: _____

     Dark: _____

AoV: After the storm, the pirate ship is lost at sea.

     Light: _____

     Dark: _____

AoV: Norman Nopants woke up and found that someone had raided the fridge and eaten all his ingredients! *"Nyet! No nuts, no nougat, no nutritious nectars?!"*

     Light: _____

     Dark: _____

AoV: Someone broke Monkey Monica's favorite doll.

     Light: _____

     Dark: _____

AoV: The forest is on fire.

     Light: _____

     Light: _____

     Dark: _____

     Dark: _____

Do you see how Light and Dark characters don't necessarily need to have anything to do with the character being good or bad?

We call them Light and Dark because actual light and darkness are opposed to one another. If one wants to make a room bright, the other wants to keep it dark. Light and Dark characters will be in conflict with one another because they have opposite goals.

SHADOWS: PARTIAL LIGHT AND PARTIAL DARK

Many characters are not *all* Light or *all* Dark. Instead, they stand in the shadows. Part of them is against the Act of Villainy and part of them is for it.

Characters like this are conflicted. At times they support the Act of Villainy and at other times they work to defeat it. But, ultimately, they fall on one side of the dividing line.

Let's look more closely at the characters in the story of Monkey Marco and the blue skunk. Connect each of these five characters to one of these four perspectives:

_____ Monkey Marco   a. Wants Marco to be clean (Light)

_____ The skunk.   b. Wants Marco's smell to go away for selfish reasons (Light shadows)

_____ Plaquebeard   c. Wants to keep going and deal with smell later (Dark shadows)

_____ Captian Yogger   d. Wants Marco to stink (Dark)

_____ Missy Monkey

We now have five characters on the spectrum of Light to Dark.

Place the number of Monkey Marco (1), the skunk (2), Plaquebeard (3), Captain Yogger (4), and Missy Monkey (5) on the following line, approximately where you think they fall in relationship to this AoV. (Remember, this has nothing to do with them being good or bad characters.)

_____|_____

DARK   DARK SHADOWS   DIVIDING LINE   LIGHT SHADOWS   LIGHT

Let's look at this AoV again: The school deans decide dancing won't be allowed at this year's annual "welcome-back-to-school" party.

Re-examine this list of characters, and place the number of each character on the Light to Dark Spectrum below.

1. The chaperones who feel bad for the kids.
2. The principal who doesn't like dancing.
3. The cool kid who hates dances.
4. The shy boy who never learned to dance.
5. The adventurous girl who loves to dance.
6. The girl who dreamed of dancing at the party but who agrees with the decision.
7. The boy and girl who want to have their first dance.

_____|_____

DARK   DARK SHADOWS   DIVIDING LINE   LIGHT SHADOWS   LIGHT

Remember when you, Scurvy Spat, tried to sneak off from swabbing the deck with Monkey Monica and Monkey Maxine? That was a story that didn't go so well for you. The characters in that story – you, Monkey Monica, Monkey Maxine, the Captain, and Mini Mate – were divided on the perspective of whether or not you should obey the orders.

Can you identify where everyone was divided in that situation?

But, first you have to identify the AoV: _____

_____

Place Monkey Monica (1), Monkey Maxine (2), the Captain (3), Mini Mate (4), and you – Scurvy Spat (5) – on the following spectrum:

_____|_____

DARK   DARK SHADOWS   DIVIDING LINE   LIGHT SHADOWS   LIGHT

Remember how there was tension between all of you, because some thought they should get to do what they wanted without getting into trouble and some wanted everyone to obey. Remember how you struggled to decide if you should stay and clean the deck or go off and take a nap? That was a tension within yourself. You didn't know which side of the line you were going to be on.

Think of six characters who fall somewhere on the Light-Dark spectrum in relation to the following Acts of Villainy. Create a mix of Light and Dark characters. Describe something about each one.

AoV: A group of bank robbers hold everyone inside the bank hostage.

    Character 1: Chuck, one of the robbers, wants money like a taco wants salsa.

    Character 2: Charlie, a hostage, doesn't want to get hurt, but he can't wait to tell all his friends what happened to him.

    Character 3: _____

    Character 4: _____

    Character 5: _____

Now place these five characters on the following spectrum.

_____|_____

DARK   DARK SHADOWS   DIVIDING LINE   LIGHT SHADOWS   LIGHT

AoV: A box full of ancient dragon eggs was discovered at the bottom of a mine.

    Character 1: _____

    Character 2: _____

    Character 3: _____

    Character 4: _____

    Character 5: _____

Now place these five characters on the following spectrum.

_____|_____

DARK   DARK SHADOWS   DIVIDING LINE   LIGHT SHADOWS   LIGHT

AoV: The elderly grandfather passes away and leaves his fortune to his children.

Character 1: _____

Character 2: _____

Character 3: _____

Character 4: _____

Character 5: _____

Now place these five characters on the following spectrum.

```
_____|_____
DARK        DARK SHADOWS      DIVIDING LINE    LIGHT SHADOWS    LIGHT
```

AoV: Five monkeys went to the amusement park, but when they got to the roller coaster, they discovered that there was only enough room on it for four, and it was the last ride of the day.

Character 1: _____

Character 2: _____

Character 3: _____

Character 4: _____

Character 5: _____

Now place these five characters on the following spectrum.

```
_____|_____
DARK        DARK SHADOWS      DIVIDING LINE    LIGHT SHADOWS    LIGHT
```

In a story, every character will fall somewhere on this line. It's important to know where they fit in order to tell a balanced story. If you have too many Dark or Dark shadow characters, your story might be really sad and depressing. Likewise, if you have too many Light and Light shadows characters, the story may not have much conflict. Placing all your characters on the spectrum can help you find the mix and balance you want for the story.

SCRATCH YER NOGGIN'

Let's see how good that memory of yours is:

1. What three things make a setting?

_____   _____   _____

2. List six values a culture might have:

_____   _____

_____   _____

_____   _____

3. What are worldlings? _____
Give three examples of a worldling.

_____   _____   _____

4. What do we call the history of a character? _____

5. What do we call the main problem in a story that the characters are trying to liquidate?

_____

6. Define characterizations: _____
List six possible characterizations for your parents, a close friend, or someone in your family:

_____   _____

_____   _____

_____   _____

7. Character values are a _____ kind of characterization.
List six possible character values for your parents, a close friend, or someone in your family:

_____   _____

_____   _____

_____   _____

RAISE THE ANCHOR AND SET SAIL

You can write any story you like. To help you get going, you can think of a couple characters and some characterizations for them. Does one of them have a problem or AoV they want to solve? Create four characters, two on the side of Light and two on the side of Dark.

_____

_____

_____

_____

_____

_____

_____

_____

_____

_____

_____

_____

_____

_____

_____

_____

_____

_____

_____

_____

_____

_____

_____

_____

_____

_____

CHAPTER AVAST AYE ARGH

That morning, as you come up onto the deck for exercises, you see all the monkeys gathered at the side of the boat looking at something down in the water.

"Who is it?" you hear Monkey Mackenzie ask.

"I no know," Monkey Monica replies casually.

"He dress weird," Missy Monkey snickers.

You get closer, but can't see what they're all looking at. All the monkeys are blocking your view, so you stand on your tiptoes to peer over them.

Sitting cross-legged and floating on a plank of wood is another monkey!

This monkey has dark black fur, with patches of white on his elbows. He wears what looks like a black cowboy hat and has dark, red-tinted sunglasses over his eyes. He wears only red beach shorts and has a matching tie around his neck.

"Yo," he calls up at all the monkeys, "you guys gonna let me up?"

The monkey mates murmur amongst themselves.

"This has never happened before," one says.

"What we do?".

"Who could he be?"

As if sensing the need for help, Captain Yogger kicks open his cabin door and comes strolling out.

"Good mornin', me hearties!" he grins.

"Cap, Cap!" Monkey Mo Mo runs over, grabs Captain Yogger's hand, and leads him to the side of the ship. "Danger! Look! Stranger!"

Captain Yogger stares down at the monkey.

"Ahoy," he calls.

"Yo," the monkey replies.

This causes a murmur amongst the monkey mates again.

"Why he say 'yo' all the time?"

"Like, 'yo, ho, ho?'"

"He talk strange."

Captain Yogger repositions his hat on his head.

"Where ye from, mate?"

"Dunno," the strange monkey replies, "woke up here."

"Aye, but where ye be from? Who are ye?" Captain Yogger asks again.

"I already say, I dunno, yo," the monkey sighs and stands up. The monkey mates gasp; he looks like he's at least a foot taller than all of them. He seems to be some different sort of breed of monkey, one you've never seen before.

"You don't even know your name?" you ask him.

"No. I wake up with a bump on my skull, yo, and no memories," he says. "All gone. I been just floating out here for days."

Captain Yogger strokes his chin as he ponders those words.

"I see."

You can't help but feel curious. Not only is there a mysterious new monkey, but it seems he's as confused as you felt when you first arrived here.

"Are we going to pull him up?" you ask.

"Hmm. Should I?" Captain Yogger leans over the edge to get a closer look at the monkey. "What do ye think? Do ye be wantin' t' be a part o' me crew?"

The monkey shrugs.

"What kind of crew, yo? What's your thing?"

Captain Yogger grins from ear to ear.

"Storytellin', mate. An' our quest be fer jelly beans."

The monkey works his mouth back and forth as if debating internally whether or not he's interested in that. You don't understand why there would be any hesitation.

"It's pretty great!" you yell to the strange monkey.

He looks up at you, blows air out of his mouth, and shrugs.

"All right, yo."

Captain Yogger turns to Monkey Mackenzie.

"Get th' net."

"Aye, aye!" Monkey Mackenzie spins on his heels and rushes away.

"Aye, mate," Captain Yogger calls down to the monkey, "what should we be callin' ye?"

The monkey shrugs again.

"Maybe we should call him Shruggy?" Missy Monkey snickers.

"That no start with 'm!'" Mini Mate snaps.

"Why not call him...Monkey M?" you suggest.

Missy Monkey bursts out laughing.

"Dumb name," she cackles.

"Ya har! I like it," Captain Yogger slaps you on the back. "Someone get Monkey M a towel an' prepare some warm food. He been out t' sea a long time."

EXERCISE #15: MYSTERY

Make of list of mysteries. I'll start with some of mine:

1.   Why do we stink when we eat bananas while other monkeys do not?

2.   Why can monkeys speak in this world, but cannot in Scurvy Spat's world?

3.   Am I going to like the sequel to my favorite movie that's coming out next year?

4.   What is in that big box with my name on it under the Christmas tree?

5.   Why does Captain Yogger speak the way he does?

6.   What's going to happen to me after I die?

7.   What's Norman Nopants' middle name?

8.   Will I ever understand quantum mechanics?

9.   _____

10. _____

11. _____

12. _____

13. _____

14. _____

15. _____

16. _____

17. _____

18. _____

19. _____

20. _____

A good story is like a box that mysteriously appears on your front door with your name on it. You wonder what's inside, who sent it, and why.

Every story begins with a mystery; what is this story about? Am I going to like it? Then, once you decide you like it, mystery keeps you going. *Mystery fuels our curiosity; it captures our attention and keeps us engaged. Mystery isn't essential for a story, but it makes it more gripping.*

Any of the elements we examined in world building – setting, significant objects, rules, values, backstory, connections – can be a source of mystery.

Look at the list of places in the left column below. Each is a potential mystery.

Connect each place on the left with some discovery about it on the right.

_____ The corner store…	a. Is hiding a family of talking mice!
_____ The old, abandoned school…	b. Is a prison for a monster!
_____ The dark and creepy mansion…	c. Is a hiding spot for thugs!
_____ The local ice cream shop…	d. Is the birthplace of dragons!
_____ The foggy island…	e. Exists entirely in the character's mind!
_____ The ancient village…	f. Is the secret home of vampires!
_____ A strange hole in the ground…	g. Where basketball players train in private!
_____ The top floor of the building…	h. Is the former home of Abraham Lincoln!

Many of your combinations would be unusual or unexpected. Who would imagine that the former home of Abraham Lincoln would be turned into a local ice cream shop? One might expect a dark and creepy mansion might be the home of vampires, but what if it was where basketball players trained?

Below is a list of significant objects. Mindstorm unexpected discoveries that might be made about the one you choose.

Significant object (choose one): Play doh / Tub of Legos / Box of crayons

Unexpected discovery: _____

Unexpected discovery: _____

Unexpected discovery: _____

Significant object (choose one): Peach / Hamburger / Bag of three-year-old frunch fries

Unexpected discovery: _____

Unexpected discovery: _____

Unexpected discovery: _____

Significant object (choose one): Blender / Old television / Table lamp

Unexpected discovery: _____

Unexpected discovery: _____

Unexpected discovery: _____

MYSTERY AND CHARACTERIZATION

An unexpected discovery is an unexpected characterization. Remember what a characterization is? Expected characterizations about a bicycle include: inflatable tires, handle bars, pedals, a mode of transportation, and a single seat. We don't expect a bicycle to fly, be invisible, or taste like peppermint. These are normal characterizations for other things (an airplane, oxygen, and tea) but they are surprising characterizations for a bicycle.

Mysteries arise when something or someone is given an unusual, unexpected, or unimaginable characterization.

Think of some great mysteries of history. No one could imagine how big the universe was. No one could fathom how small the elementary particles of matter were. No one could believe someone could ride a kraken (and survive).

Make up some incredible, unbelievable things about the following:

1. Example: Everything about the laws of gravity changed when Monkey Michelangelo threw a 13-year-old banana peel up into the sky at midnight on Summer Solstice and it never came back down.

2. When scientists discovered _____, they were able to create unlimited energy.

3. Cats are really _____.

4. Every child would be flying to school using jet packs if only

_____.

5. No one imagined if you combined milk with _____ it would make

_____!

6. No one expected that the frightening dragon was actually just _____ and only seemed angry because _____!

7. When Orangutan Ollie and Omar first met the Dread Pirate Plaquebeard, they were

_____. But together, they learned the value of _____ and have been inseparable ever since.

8. The truth about the moon is that it's actually _____.

9: Two humans showed up at my house and told me that I was a _____, and that if I didn't come with them immediately, then _____ would happen!

10. That morning, when I woke up, I discovered that my parents had been turned into

_____!

MYSTERY AND CHARACTER

The greatest source of mystery in story is characters.

As you learned in the sections on characterization, characters have many traits. When you first meet someone, you know very little about them; they are a mystery to you. But, as you get to know them and their characterizations, they become less of a mystery.

Write the first name that pops into your head: _____

Now, write the first characterization you think of: _____

Now, write down an age: _____ A disease a person can have: _____

A country: _____ A food: _____ A hair color: _____

A job: _____ A hobby: _____

Imagine a character who has these traits/characterizations. When you first wrote their name, they were a complete mystery. But, as you added details, things became clearer, although there are still mysteries; you may wonder about the disease they have, or something you wrote about them that was unexpected or strange.
What are some other things you would want to know about this character?

_____

_____

Think of a name: _____ Think of a fruit: _____

A fast food restaurant: _____ An hourly wage: _____

Now, write down an age: _____ A height: _____ A weight: _____

Now, imagine this character having a job working at this fast food restaurant dressed up in a costume of this fruit. Can you picture them? Do you think they like this job? Why do you think they are doing it? Would you do this job for the hourly wage you listed?

On the left are some characters, and on the right are some characterizations. Connect a character with a detail you think would make for an interesting discovery!

_____ A boring math teacher. . .   a. Is an undercover police officer!
_____ A very private new neighbor. . .   b. Is an evil spy!
_____ A cat with shifty eyes. . . .   c. Is a millionaire!
_____ A homeless person with a golden violin. . . d. Cannot read!
_____ A pirate who never seems to sleep. . .   e. Built a time machine!
_____ A talkative stranger on the bus. . .   f. Owns a baby pet dinosaur!
_____ A child who is always late to class. . .   g. Has the ability to read minds!
_____ A grumpy mall clerk. . .   h. Has a lost child!
_____ A silent football player. . .   i. Can speak nine languages!

Now your turn. Describe an unusual, unexpected, or surprising characterization for the following characters. I'll do the first two for you.

1. The shy, new boy in school . . . is really an alien!

2. The girl who walks with a limp . . . has a leg made out of solid gold!

3. No matter where he goes, dogs bark at Malachi. . .

_____

4. The patient in the hospital who doesn't remember his name. . .

_____

5. The Secret Service Agent locked up in a hotel room. . .

_____

6. The dancer who never dances. . .

_____

7. The artist who only paints in shades of blue or red. . .

_____

Now I want you to do the opposite. But, first I want you to create a list of ten of your favorite fictional characters.

1. _____   6. _____

2. _____   7. _____

3. _____   8. _____

4. _____   9. _____

5. _____   10. _____

Write down the name of a character from your list that would create a mystery if true.

1. _____ . . . is afraid no one takes them seriously.

2. _____ . . . was born into a poor family!

3. _____ . . . is the dictator of a country in South-East Osia!

4. _____'s . . . voice can break windows when singing!

5. _____ . . . is a master of many martial arts!

6. _____ . . . is a former prisoner who escaped from jail!

7. _____ . . . was bitten by a vampire!

WHO IS THIS CHARACTER?

A character does not need to have some crazy, impossible-to-believe characterization to create mystery. There is plenty of mystery in everyday, ordinary characters. It may be as simple as the mystery of why your good friend is looking sad today. Or the mystery of why your math teacher, who used to be dry and boring, became funny and dynamic after winter break.

Write the name of someone you know well: _____

What would you be surprised to learn about this person? (Think of ordinary things.)

Something they know how to do:

_____

Some place they want to travel to:

_____

A favorite food:

_____

Someone they know well:

_____

Something that makes them cry:

_____

Where they were born:

_____

Something they are afraid of:

_____

Something they dream of doing:

_____

If we care about a character we will want to know more about them, especially if an element of mystery surrounds them. Likewise, if there is an element of mystery with a character it can lead us to want to understand that mystery, which, in turn, causes us to care about them.

Here are some questions you might ask when first meeting a character (think of three more):

- What do they know?
- What do they want?
- What can they do?
- What are they afraid of?
- What are their relationships?
- Where are they from?
- What are they, really?

- What is their backstory?
- Why are they in this story?
- Why did they do what they did?
- Why do they act the way they do?

_____

_____

_____

Think of one of your favorite characters from a story: _____

Take three questions from the above list and answer them about this character.

1. _____

_____

2. _____

_____

3. _____

_____

Think of one of your favorite characters from a story: _____

Take three questions from the above list and answer them about this character.

1. _____

_____

2. _____

_____

3. _____

_____

REVEALING THE ANSWERS

One key aspect to mystery is the reveal; when do you choose to let your audience know the truth?

Think about the days leading up to Christmas. There are a bunch of presents with your name on them under the tree, and you can't help but wonder what you got. But peeking early is no good! If you eliminate the mystery before the right time, it'll spoil the fun on Christmas morning.

In the same way, part of the fun in a story is discovering the answers and solving the mystery in the proper time. It wouldn't be much fun reading a book or watching a movie if someone had spoiled the ending, would it? In order to get the fullest enjoyment, you'll want to preserve the mystery until the best possible time to reveal it.

1. When is the proper time to take a bite out of your birthday cake?

_____

2. When is the proper time to know about a surprise party, if you are the person being surprised?

_____

3. When is the proper time to find out who won a competition?

_____

4. When is the proper time to ask if someone wants to be friends?

_____

5. When is the proper time to find out how the movie will end?

_____

FORESHADOWING

One technique the storyteller can use to help build mystery is to give a bit of something we call foreshadowing. These are little hints or references to something that will happen later on. Foreshadowing keeps us interested, it keeps us guessing, it gives us a little glimpse at the solution to the mystery without giving the whole thing away.

What are some hints that might foreshadow the flavor of your birthday cake?

1. _____

2. _____

3. _____

What are some hints that might foreshadow a surprise party?

1. _____

2. _____

3. _____

What are some hints that might foreshadow who will win a competition?

1. _____

2. _____

3. _____

What are some hints that might foreshadow if someone is ready to be friends?

1. _____

2. _____

3. _____

What are some hints that might foreshadow how the movie will end?

1. _____

2. _____

3. _____

Mystery should be deliciously frustrating. Like a spice, it has the ability to increase the flavor of a story. It can make hearing a story for the first time really exciting because it makes us want to know what will happen!

CHAPTER AVAST ARGH

"It been long enough!" Monkey Martin snaps.

"No," First Mate Manfred crosses his arms, "you still smell."

"So! Everyone smell!"

It's about an hour before bed, and as you approach your room, you find Monkey Morgan and Monkey Morta standing in front of the door. Inside, Monkey Martin and First Mate Manfred are opposite one another in the middle of the room having what looks to be a very heated argument.

"What's going on?" you ask cautiously as you peek your head through the doorway.

"Get lost, Spat." Monkey Morgan grabs you by your shoulders and pulls you back into the hall. "This don't concern you."

"Yeah!" Monkey Morta echoes.

"This is my room, too," you reply.

The two monkeys look at one another and scratch their heads.

"Oh yeah," Monkey Morta scrunches up her face.

"Just be quiet then!" Monkey Morgan warns.

You nod, and the three of you look through the doorway.

"How long you plan to make us sleep on th' deck?" Monkey Martin shouts at First Mate Manfred.

"For as long as it takes for the bean to pass out of your system," the First Mate states rather matter-of-factly.

"What bean?" Monkey Martin suddenly sounds very innocent, "I got me no idea what you talkin' about."

"Yes, you do," First Mate Manfred sighs, "I'm no fool, I didn't learn how to speak yesterday. I know you three stole some of Captain Yogger's jelly beans and ate them."

"Who told you that!" Monkey Martin clenches his fists. "Was it Spat!?"

"No. You told me that."

"I did not! I never say anything."

"You didn't have to. Your new terrible smell gave you away."

Monkey Martin looks like he's about to explode with anger.

"Okay. So what?" he sneers. "We found a bean and ate it. Who cares? Not like he cares. We be going to get a whole lot more soon enough, as long as LeFossa don't horde them all for himself."

First Mate Manfred leans forward and bares his teeth.

"You watch what you say and think carefully about your next words," he warns with a look of wild fury in his eye. "I have no patience for cheaters and liars, and even less for those who try to take advantage of Captain Yogger or mock him behind his back."

It gets deadly silent in the room, and even you feel afraid. This is the first time you've ever seen the First Mate look angry or raise his voice.

"Hey!" Monkey Martin swallows nervously. "Careful. LeFossa made me part o' this crew!"

"Yes, indeed he did. And with that come certain responsibilities and expectations. Continue to defy the rules, and your time on this ship will be short lived." First Mate Manfred leans back, straightens his shirt, and heads toward the exit. But, before he walks through, he looks over his shoulder and adds a few final words: "A few more days and you'll be good to sleep in your own room again. But, be careful. I'm watching you three closely."

You and the other two monkeys quickly slide out of the way as the first mate storms past. You're now quite grateful the other monkeys didn't cut you a piece of that jelly bean.

"So, we sleep on deck again?" Monkey Morta asks.

"Aye. A few more nights," Monkey Martin grumbles as he enters the hall. When he sees you, he winces.

"Enjoy the room all to yerself," he grumbles under his breath as he and the others walk away, leaving you standing alone outside your room.

EXERCISE #16: CHARACTER CONTRADICTIONS

I'm going to tell you a secret. I don't like the water. I never liked swimming, and I generally avoid getting wet. I like sea water even less. But, here I am on a boat in the middle of the ocean. I won't tell you why; I'll leave that as a mystery. I share this with you because I want you to understand something.

Characters don't always make sense; they can have contradictions.

Here is one you already know about: us monkey mates aren't allowed to eat bananas. Who ever heard of a monkey who shouldn't eat bananas? Well, you're surrounded by them.

Think of some possible contradictions for the following characters.

1.   A toothless ninety-year old man who _____

2.   An evil pirate captain who _____

3.   An apple farmer who _____

4.   A dog that doesn't like to eat _____ and instead eats _____

5.   A talented singer who can't _____

6.   A doctor who never _____

7.   A pilot who loves to _____

8.   A teacher who never learned how to _____

9.   The President of Canmerico who has a habit of _____

10. A child who has never played with _____

On the left are some careers, and on the right are some characteristics. Connect the things you think could be an interesting contradiction.

_____ Police officer

_____ Fire fighter

_____ Astronaut

_____ Artist

_____ Musician

_____ Doctor

a. Scared of space

b. Dislikes music

c. Colorblind

d. Cowardly

e. Clumsy

f. Selfish

DIFFERENT ENVIRONMENTS

Oftentimes characters – and people – are different in different environments. Monkeys act different at a coconut football match than they do at the MonkeyWood Symphony.

Monkey Mary really loves dancing. But, she's very shy and fears the other monkeys will laugh at her. So, whenever we get together to dance on Wednesday nights, she just watches quietly, even though dancing is her favorite thing!

What are some locations/places/environments where Monkey Mary might feel safe to dance?

1. _____   4. _____
2. _____   5. _____
3. _____   6. _____

Monkey Martin insists he doesn't cry and has never cried in his life. But once, while we were watching the movie "The Monkey with No Home," I saw a tear trickle down his face.

What are some locations/places/environments where Monkey Martin might cry?

1. _____   4. _____
2. _____   5. _____
3. _____   6. _____

What is a different country you have thought you would like to visit: _____

What are some things you might need to do differently if you traveled to this country?

1. _____   4. _____
2. _____   5. _____
3. _____   6. _____

DIFFERENT CIRCUMSTANCES

Characters will express different characterizations based on their circumstances. Monkey Mo Mo usually feels safe and comfortable when he's on the ship. But, whenever the ship is about to enter a thick fog, fear takes control of him. He stops thinking clearly and is tempted to do foolish things, like jump overboard.

What are some other kinds of circumstances that might cause Monkey Mo Mo to get scared?

1. _____   4. _____

2. _____   5. _____

3. _____   6. _____

Captain Yogger believes early morning exercise is a valuable way to start the day!

What are some circumstances that might cause Captain Yogger to cancel the morning exercises for a day?

1. _____   4. _____

2. _____   5. _____

3. _____   6. _____

Most families take time to have celebrations. It may be for a holiday, or to honor someone's achievement, a special birthday, a family reunion, or something else. What is an occasion that your family celebrates? _____

List some ways people in your family act differently due to the circumstances of having a celebration.

1. _____   3. _____

2. _____   4. _____

DIFFERENT RELATIONSHIPS

The relationships between various characters can be a way story creators reveal the different characterizations of their characters. Simply put, a character may act quite differently with each different person.

For example, you know me as First Mate Manfred. Your primary experience with me is as your teacher. I am clean, proper, and not so very monkey-like when I'm teaching class. But, when I'm not teaching, and hanging out with Norman Nopants, I find myself getting quite rambunctious, silly, and lazy. Then, when I serve Captain Yogger as first mate, I am forceful, serious, and sometimes scream at others to do exactly as they are told.

All of these things are true parts of who I am. It's just that certain characters and circumstances bring out these different – and contradictory – aspects in me. For example, I wouldn't be a very good teacher if I screamed at you, or fell asleep teaching class. Nor would I be a good first mate if I acted silly and irresponsible around Captain Yogger.

Monkey Maxine hated brushing her teeth and refused to ever do it. Then one day, she went to a new dentist who helped her understand why she needed to take care of her teeth. What other kinds of relationships might make Monkey Maxine agree to brush her teeth?

1. _____   3. _____

2. _____   4. _____

Norman normally refuses to eat non-"n" food. But, there are some people who would cause him to change his mind. Who might cause Norman to eat other foods?

1. _____   3. _____

2. _____   4. _____

Mini Mate acts pretty impatient and unkind to you, poor Spat, but with Monkey Mo Mo, Mini Mate is gentle and kind. Both kindness and meanness are characterizations of Mini Mate, but they only come out around certain characters.

This is true for everyone. Different people draw out different aspects of us. You behave one way with your mom and another with your friend. Think of the all the people in your life: your mom, dad, grandmother, your aunt or a cousin. Think of your friends, people you don't like, and enemies – if you have any. Think about your teachers, neighbors, and people you might interact with like shopkeepers, waiters, police, librarians and any number of different types of people.

When you are with _____, what characterizations come out of you?

_____

When you are with _____, what characterizations come out of you?

_____

When you are with _____, what characterizations come out of you?

_____

When you are with _____, what characterizations come out of you?

_____

When you are with _____, what characterizations come out of you?

_____

When you are with _____, what characterizations come out of you?

_____

When you create a character and give them a characterization you want to make sure you also have another character in the story who will bring out that characterization of your character.

As a story creator, you want to reveal to the audience that characters have all these differing – and sometimes conflicting – characterizations inside them.

Try being a story creator right now. Let's say you wanted Captain Yogger to have three new characterizations: annoyed, fearful, and romantic. Create three new characters who would draw out these new sides of the captain's character:

1. Create and describe a character that could reveal the captain's annoyed side.

_____

_____

_____

2. Describe a character that could reveal the captain's fearful side.

_____

_____

_____

3. Describe a character that could reveal the captain's romantic side.

_____

_____

_____

>   *From outside the classroom, you hear a loud shout,*
>   *"Shiver me timbers! No need t' be creatin' romance in me! Yuck! Ain't a captain's only love fer th' sea?"*

Having a wide variety of characters in a story gives a story creator an opportunity to reveal a wide variety of characterizations in all their characters.

Not every single side of a character needs to come out in a story. For example, you already know several different sides of my character. But, you haven't seen me silly. For all you know I never get silly. But, on occasion I do. It takes a certain sort of monkey to draw it out of me, but it happens. (For example, no one makes me more silly than my crazy-wild-pineapple-gobbling cousin, Malcolm. Lucky for us he isn't on this ship, or you might really see my silly side.)

Can you think of anyone who you've never seen silly? _____

Can you think of someone who might make them silly?_____

Can you think of anyone who you've never seen sad? _____

Can you think of someone who might make them sad?_____

Can you think of anyone who you've never seen afraid? _____

Can you think of a circumstance that might make them afraid? _____

EMOTIONS

Mindstorm a list of emotions here:

1. _____   9. _____
2. _____   10. _____
3. _____   11. _____
4. _____   12. _____
5. _____   13. _____
6. _____   14. _____
7. _____   15. _____
8. _____   16. _____

Emotions change all the time. One moment we might be happy and the next sad. Courage can turn to fear in an instant. One day we may jump out of bed full of vigor and enthusiasm. The next day we may be so sad that we keep the covers over our head all morning.

1. Choose two emotions from your list A. _____ B. _____

Write about a character and what causes them to switch from feeling emotion A to emotion B:

_____

_____

_____

2. Choose two more emotions from your list A. _____ B. _____

Write about a character and what causes them to switch from feeling emotion A to emotion B:

_____

_____

_____

Now describe how they go back to feeling emotion A:

_____

_____

_____

3. Choose two emotions from your list A. _____ B. _____

Write about a character and what causes them to switch from feeling emotion A to emotion B:

_____

_____

_____

Chose another emotion from your list. C. _____

Now describe how your character changes from feeling emotion B to emotion C:

_____

_____

_____

One of my favorite stories is *The Adventures of Tom Sawyer.* In it there are many different characters who bring out different emotions in Tom.

    Annoyed — Sid: Tom's whiny half-brother

    Excitement — Huckleberry Finn: Tom's best friend

    Fear — Injun Joe: A scary murderer

    Love — Becky: A beautiful girl

    Anger — Mr. Dobbins: Their hated teacher

    Happiness — Aunt Polly: His loving aunt

Now think of a character from a story you like, and choose two emotions from the list. Write down two other characters from the same story that draw out those emotions in the character you picked, like I just did with Tom Sawyer.

Story: _____ Character: _____

Emotion 1: _____ Character who reveals this emotion: _____

Emotion 2: _____ Character who reveals this emotion: _____

Now do it again with two other stories.

Story: _____ Character: _____

Emotion 1: _____ Character who reveals this emotion: _____

Emotion 2: _____ Character who reveals this emotion: _____

186

Story: _____ Character: _____

Emotion 1: _____ Character who reveals this emotion: _____

Emotion 2: _____ Character who reveals this emotion: _____

CONTRADICTORY DESIRES

Have you been wondering why I became a pirate if I don't like the water? The answer has to do with my values. I value serving Captain Yogger more than I value staying away from the water. Desires and values are closely related. I value – or desire – to stay dry, but I also desire to seek treasure, teach story, and fight kraken with the captain.

Desires, as we will see later, cause characters to make choices and to change.

1. Monkey Monica may hate brushing her teeth, but she also hates getting cavities. This will force her to make a choice based on what she desires more. What choice do you think she will make the week before her next dentist visit? _____. What choice do you think she will make during Halloween? _____

2. Orangutan Omar and Orangutan Ollie want to be naughty, but they also want to make their mom proud. What choice do you think they will make when their mom is watching? _____ _____What about when they are sailing with Captain Plaquebeard? _____

3. Monkey Mo Mo wants to be safe, but he also wants to help Captain Yogger find his magic jelly beans. What do you think these two conflicting desires will cause him to do if he becomes very scared while searching for the magic beans? _____

_____

_____

4. Norman Nopants wants to make _____ for supper, but he also wants to make _____(something that does not go with the other food). What could cause him to choose the second over the first? _____

_____

_____

Here is a list of random characterizations. Add some of your own.

Rascally	Anti-social	Cross-eyed	_____
Hard-Working	Grey-haired	Fast runner	_____
Fashionable	Out-of-shape	Skilled dancer	_____
Athletic	Lazy	Can't sing	_____
Risky	Always bored	Lives in a shoe	_____
Responsible	Young	Adventurous	_____
Brown-eyed	Life of the party	Hates music	_____
Easily-angered	Spiky-haired	Is an entertainer	_____
Funny	Glows	Sleepy	_____
Speaks slowly	Webbed toes	Afraid of the dark	_____

Explain one reason why someone would be a skilled dancer and out of shape:

_____

_____

Explain how someone can be an entertainer and anti-social: _____

_____

How can someone be hard-working and lazy? _____

_____

Can you think of a second reason? _____

_____

What about someone who is young but has grey hair? _____

_____

Can you think of a second reason? _____

_____

Now choose two characterizations from the list above that don't seem to match up and give two explanations of how they can still remain true for one person.

Trait: _____ Trait: _____

Explanation #1 _____

_____

Explanation #2 _____

_____

Trait: _____ Trait: _____

Explanation #1 _____

_____

Explanation #2 _____

_____

Now you know that there can be contradictory characterizations in a character and why it is valuable for a story creator to understand how these contradictions can exist together.

SCRATCH YER NOGGIN'

Test your memory! Look back only if you need to.

1. Being specific is a way of setting _____ and creating a _____.

2. Things can be made more specific by adding _____.

3. Rules determine what can and cannot _____ in the _____.

4. Symbols enable _____, but only if people understand what the symbol means.

5. What are some ways the monkey mates are connected to Captain Yogger?

_____   _____

_____   _____

_____   _____

6. Values are things that are _____.

7. What reveals our values? _____

8. _____ are essential for a story, because they create conflict.

9. For all characters, the _____ becomes the dividing line that separates them on two different sides, _____ or _____.

10. What side are the characters on who are in favor of the Act of Villainy? _____

11. What side are the characters on who are opposed to the Act of Villainy? _____

12. Some characters are conflicted and stand somewhere between the two extremes, but are still on either side of the dividing line. What do we call these characters?

_____ and _____.

CHAPTER AVAST ARGH AYE

You stand on the deck letting the fresh air wash over you as you watch the sunset in the distance. Watching a sunset over the ocean is different than anything you've experienced at home. Here, with the water reflecting the beautiful oranges and reds, you feel as though you are truly witnessing something incredible.

But the moment of serenity doesn't last long.

"Land ho!"

What? Can it be?

You look around, yet see nothing but water for miles and miles.

"Really?" Monkey Monica says as she wanders by. She looks as confused as you.

"Land ho! Land ho!" Mini Mate practically screams as he leaps down from the top of the mast with a golden telescope under his arm.

Several other monkeys hear the news and start to get excited, but you still feel confused; there's no land anywhere.

"I'm comin', I'm comin'," Captain Yogger grumbles as he bursts out of his private cabin.

"Give me that!" he snatches the golden telescope away from Mini Mate and uses it to stare off into the distance.

"Do you see it? Is he right?" one of the monkeys eagerly asks.

"Aye. 'Tis a good sight," Captain Yogger grins. "See fer yerself, mates."

He hands the telescope to Missy Monkey, who takes it eagerly and looks through.

"I can see it! I can see it!" she squeals with delight and jumps up and down.

"My turn!" Monkey Martin snatches it and takes a look. "Har har! It there, all right! Ooohhh yeah . . . It there."

You can't believe it; how far could that telescope possibly see?

"Me next!" Monkey Monica exclaims. The telescope is finally passed to her and she peaks through.

"Huh?" she looks confused, then hands you the telescope and laughs. "Har har! Very funny. Some joke."

"What?"

"They lie. Very funny," Monkey Monica laughs again to herself and struts away.

"It bein' no joke!" Mini Mate hisses. "It be real! Look again!"

"Nah, nah. I no be fooled twice!" she chuckles and wanders back into the lower levels with a few of the other monkeys who apparently didn't see anything either.

Is it really a joke?

You lift the telescope to your eye and peer through; it takes you a few seconds, but then – sure enough – you see a massive, sparkling island materialize on the sea. It's beautiful, lush and green, with a white, sandy beach and rocky, obsidian cliffs.

But wait, how can it be there? You lower the telescope and it's gone, but when you raise it, you can see the island.

"Is it magic?" you whisper in awe as Monkey Mackenzie takes the telescope from you to have a look.

"I . . . don't. . ." Monkey Mackenzie pulls it away, squints, and tries again. "I see nothing but water." He sounds miserable.

"Me try?" Monkey Mo Mo asks.

He takes the telescope in both hands and looks through.

"I . . . see it." Monkey Mo Mo puts down the telescope and takes a few steps away.

"What's wrong?" you ask.

"I don't know why no all see."

Mini Mate grabs the telescope and hands it back to Monkey Mackenzie. "Try again."

Monkey Mackenzie looks through again, but when he lowers the telescope, his shoulders sag.

"If it magic? Why not all see?" Monkey Mo Mo turns and scampers away.

Monkey Mackenzie looks down at his feet and sniffles.

You turn to the Captain and ask, "What's happening? I don't understand."

"Th' scope be revealin' what we desirin'," Captain Yogger answers, "some be seein' it right away, an' others may need a bit o' time."

"But, I don't see anything," Monkey Mackenzie said.

"Keep tryin'. We got lots o' time yet."

The words of the captain nearly cause Mini Mate's eyes to pop out of his head.

"What!? Lots of time?!" he exclaims. "Th' island bein' right there."

You have to admit, you feel as surprised as Mini Mate. From what you saw in the telescope the ship would be at the island in no time.

"Th' island look near, but be far, far away."

"It is?" you stammer. It doesn't make any sense.

"Aye. Part o' the magic. Fer all who be desirin' our destination, th' vision be only th' seein'. Some things be takin' time and workin' before thay be arrivin'." Captain Yogger takes the telescope and holds it up in the air. "All right, ye scurvy dogs. Th' island be out thar, waitin'. Those who no be seein' it, I want ye to keep lookin' until ye do. It's thar, mateys. So let's get heavin' an' hovin'!"

"Aye, aye," Mini Mate replies cheerfully as he takes the telescope and hands it to another monkey to look through.

EXERCISE #17: CHARACTER DESIRE

Characters have desires.

They might be hungry and want food. They might feel silly and want to play. They might be angry and want revenge. They might be sad and want a hug. Identifying a character's desires helps the author know who their characters are and what they will do.

Desires identify what a character wants.

Make a list of 20 desires.

1.   To go back and visit my old friends on Monkey Mountain.

2.   To eat as many bananas as I want.

3.   To find magic jelly beans with Captain Yogger.

4.   To ride Class 3 Kraken Kramer.

5.   _____

6.   _____

7.   _____

8.   _____

9.   _____

10. _____

11. _____

12. _____

13. _____

14. _____

15. _____

16. _____

17. _____

18. _____

19. _____

20. _____

There are all kinds of desires. They can be physical, emotional, social, villainous, etc. Some desires are common – something most people would want – and others are rare. Desires range from vague (to be happy) to very specific (to laugh out loud while dancing with my monkey mates next Wednesday evening).

List six physical desires:

1. To learn how to swim

2. _____

3. _____

4. _____

5. _____

6. _____

List six social desires:

1. To have others laugh at my jokes

2. _____

3. _____

4. _____

5. _____

6. _____

List six emotional desires:

1. To feel happy

2. _____

3. _____

4. _____

5. _____

6. _____

List six villainous desires:

1. To steal the captain's jelly beans

2. _____

3. _____

4. _____

5. _____

6. _____

List six desires that nearly everyone wants:

1. Sleep

2. _____

3. _____

4. _____

5. _____

6. _____

List six unusual desires:

1. To know what mistletoe tastes like

2. _____

3. _____

4. _____

5. _____

6. _____

List six very specific desires:

1. To feel happy in class today when everyone laughs at my joke about wanting to know what mistletoe tastes like.

2. _____

_____

3. _____

_____

4. _____

_____

5. _____

_____

CHARACTERIZATIONS LEAD TO DESIRES

Characterizations, like you've learned, describe specific things about a character.

Mini Mate is much shorter than other monkeys (a characterization). People never saw him in a crowd and as a result he developed a desire to stand out. He and his siblings were separated when they were taken as slaves at a young age, and as a result, he's always had a desire to bring the family back together.

Think of a desire for the following characters that would grow out of their characterization:

1. Susie is an only child.
She wants:

_____

2. Sadi reads a book daily.
She wants:

_____

3. Stewart is a wizard.
He wants:

_____

4. Sean cooks every night.
He wants:

_____

5. Stefan owns a dog.
He wants:

_____

6. Sofia plays basketball.
She wants:

_____

7. Seb's full name is Sebastian Sabastapole Seabass. He wants:

_____

8. Sky is shy. She wants:

_____

9. Sara is a scooter fanatic.
She wants:

_____

Now, choose three of the characters above. Come up with two more desires they might have that are <u>different</u> from what you listed above.

For example: Character: Susie is an only child.

1. Susie wants to go to summer camp where she will be part of a cabin of other girls.

2. She wants to go to the park every day after school and play with her friends.

Character: _____

1. _____

2. _____

Character: _____

1. _____

2. _____

Here is a list of characterizations:

Ticklish	Sleeps upside down
Overly serious	Is afraid of heights
Grumpy	Loves driving in a car
Addicted to sugar	Chews nails when nervous
Hairy	Doesn't know how to swim
Lives in a tree	Wears ancient jewelry
Has pointy ears	Loves to paint
Grew up on a ranch	Wears glasses
Is always warm	Speaks seven languages
Only drinks milk	Was born on a raft in the ocean

Choose any three: 1. _____ 2. _____ 3. _____

Create a character with an "S" name: _____ and their age _____

Based on this, what are two desires this character might have?

1. _____

2. _____

Choose any three: 1. _____ 2. _____ 3. _____

Create a character with an "S" name: _____ and their age _____

Based on this, what are two desires this character might have?

1. _____

2. _____

Choose any three: 1. _____ 2. _____ 3. _____

Create a character with an "S" name: _____ and their age _____

Based on this, what are two desires this character might have?

1. _____

2. _____

ONE CHARACTERIZATION, MANY DIFFERENT DESIRES

One characterization can lead to many different desires. Being short (a physical characterization) like Mini Mate might cause a character to desire to be taller, or it might lead him to want to talk like a pirate, or be strong.

Imagine a character who was nearsighted (they cannot see things that are far away). This would probably cause them to want to get glasses, but it also might cause them to desire to read books, or become a musician.

Think of two completely different desires a character could have for the following characterizations:

Characterization: Has an embarrassing laugh

1. _____   2. _____

Characterization: Is going bald

1. _____   2. _____

Characterization: Was born with a weird birthmark on their arm

1. _____   2. _____

Characterization: Never learned how to dance

1. _____   2. _____

Characterization: Was almost swallowed by a kraken

1. _____   2. _____

Characterization: Has three kids

1. _____   2. _____

Remember those identical twin orangutans I told you about, Ollie and Omar? They are the same in almost every way physically. But, they grew up to have dramatically different desires. Ollie just wants to have fun and prank people by pretending to be his brother, but Omar wants to be his own individual and rule the world.

Take a guess for three other desires these twin orangutans might have:

Ollie desires: Omar desires:

1. _____   1. _____

2. _____   2. _____

3. _____   3. _____

Believe it or not, Ollie and Omar also have two twin sisters – Olga and Orva. What do you think some of their desires might be?

Olga desires:

1. _____

2. _____

3. _____

Orva desires:

1. _____

2. _____

3. _____

DESIRES IN OPPOSITION TO CHARACTERIZATIONS

Desires describe what a person or character wants. Sometimes desires are in opposition to a person's characterizations.

Example: Marcus is out of shape; he can't walk up a flight of stairs without getting out of breath. But, Marcus has a desire: he wants to run on his school's track team.

1. Nadine is horrified of bugs; she screams every time she sees one. But, Nadine has a desire:

_____

2. Manfred (yup, that's me) doesn't like the water. But, I have a desire:

_____

3. Sammy the Slug is super slow. But, he has a desire:

_____

4. Captain Yogger was born a prince. But, he had a desire:

_____

5. Willie was born a wombat. But, he has a desire:

_____

Do the same exercise again, but this time, I'll give you the desire and you create a characterization that will make achieving that desire difficult.

Example: Omar has a desire to be an individual and rule the world, even though he has brothers and sisters who keep getting in the way.

1. Magnus has a desire to be the new monkey monarch, even though:

_____

2. Louis has a desire to live in a snowy environment, even though:

_____

3. Dread Pirate Plaquebeard has a desire to smell like a rose, even though:

_____

4. Kraken Kent has a desire to be a big, powerful kraken, even though:

_____

5. Monkey M has a desire to introduce himself to people, even though:

_____

DESIRES LEAD TO ACTIONS

Let's say you haven't eaten all day. You are hungry and you desire _____! That desire is going to cause you to take action.

You might go into your _____ and make a _____

You might go to _____ and buy _____

Our desires cause us to take action. Write what action you might take for the desires below:

1. If you desire a coconut smoothie for breakfast:

_____

2. If you want to go to the Slip-on-a-Banana Wet-and-Wild Water Park this weekend:

_____

3. If you want to rule the universe before you are forty years old:

_____

4. If you want to write a 200-page-novel in a month:

_____

5. If you want to fly around our ship like a seagull:

_____

6. If you want to see the frozen tundra of Northern Sweetishland in a rowboat pulled by yaks:

_____

7. If you want to flunk the math exam you just sat down to take:

_____

8. If you want to eat nothing but chocolate for the rest of your life:

_____

9. If you want to sleep in a castle made of ice:

_____

10. If you want to see the bottom of the ocean with your own eyes:

_____

11. If you want to travel back in time to meet a dinosaur:

_____

12. If you want to have a unique color of hair:

_____

13. If you want to learn to understand the language of dogs:

_____

14. If you want design your own clothing:

_____

15. If you want to make friends with an alligator:

_____

16. If you want to win the coconut football game:

_____

17. If you want to be a master musician:

_____

18. If you want to see every country in the world:

_____

19. If you want to wake up really early in the morning:

_____

20. If you want to get Captain Yogger to let everyone dance on more than just Wednesdays:

_____

SPECIFIC DESIRES

As I described before, one of Mini Mate's big desires is to stand out. This desire has led him to take many actions. He tried to stand out by becoming a stand-up comedian, but he stank (and on top of that no one laughed at his jokes). Next, he tried to stand out by breaking a world record. So, he became a migrant farm worker and got practice harvesting carrots, all in the hopes of breaking the world record at the World Carrot-Pulling Championships. While his small height gave him an advantage, he got carpel tunnel in his left wrist and lost. He tried and failed at many different competitions until the captain found him trying to swallow more bananas than he could stomach at the South Florinda Banana Eating Contest.

Mini Mate's vague desire to stand out led him to have many different specific desires. I just described four of them. List them:

1. _____   3. _____

2. _____   4. _____

Can you come up with four specific desires that could have come out of his other vague desire – to reunite his family?

1. _____   3. _____

2. _____   4. _____

When creating a story, you want to create specific, concrete desires for your characters.

The more specific the desire, the better it describes what a character really wants. Knowing a character's specific desire makes it easier to know if the character has gotten what they want.

Example: Serah is a jelly bean factory worker.
She has a desire to collect three jelly beans of each of the 801 flavors the factory has produced.

1. Small Beard is a pirate.

Desire: _____

2. Samantha is a chef in a pudding restaurant.

Desire: _____

3. Smarty is a high school student.

Desire: _____

4. Smasher is a gorilla who plays professional coconut football.

Desire: _____

5. Stirrup rides her horse every afternoon as soon as she finishes school.

Desire: _____

DRAMATIC DESIRES

In addition to making your character's desires specific, you also need to make them dramatic.

A dramatic desire is a desire that can be achieved because it has a fixed finish line. You know when a dramatic desire has been accomplished.

A desire such as "I want to go somewhere" is not dramatic. Somewhere could be anywhere. How do you know when you have arrived if you don't know exactly where you are going?

"I want to go somewhere" can be made dramatic by making it more specific.

    I want to ride my bike to the library.

    OR   I want to fly my space helicopter to the moon.

    OR   I want to row my boat to Big Mammon Island and look for buried loot.

There is a clear finish line to each of these desires.

Take the following vague desires and turn them into a dramatic desire by making it something that can be achieved. I'll do the first one, you do the rest.

1. Doug wants to go somewhere fun.

Doug wants to take his best friend to the gorilla rodeo next Tuesday and laugh at the rodeo clowns.

2. Dudley wants to be grumpy.

_____

3. Denise wants a pet.

_____

4. David wants to eat something crazy.

_____

5. Dolly wants to make a friend laugh.

_____

6. Daisy wants to go shopping.

_____

7. Donna wants to sing for someone.

_____

8. Deborah wants to visit a factory.

_____

9. Dakota wants to meet someone famous.

_____

10. Daniel wants to watch a movie.

_____

Dramatic desires drive a story, because desires lead a character to action.

Take these desires and make them more specific (with details) and more dramatic (something that can be achieved).

1. A doctor wants to help someone.

Example: Dr. Dermatitis wants to cure Mary Mahogany's inflexible epidermis.

2. A soldier wants to protect his country from the invading forces.

_____

_____

202

3. A girl wants to do something with her hair.

_____

_____

4. A boy wants to be cool.

_____

_____

5. A teacher wants to teach.

_____

_____

6. The tied up dog wants to go.

_____

_____

Different characters that have the same vague desire often have **different** dramatic desires.

By imagining different characters with different characterizations, **you can** come up with all kinds of ways to make a vague desire dramatic.

Someone wants to go somewhere.

1. Character: Jennifer   Characterization: Feels happiest while reading a book

Dramatic desire: Wants to ride her bike to the library.

2. Character: Joe   Characterization: _____

Dramatic desire: Wants to fly his space helicopter to the moon.

3. Character: Monkey Maddy   Characterization: _____

Dramatic desire: To row out to Mammon Island and fill her boat with _____

Take the following vague desire and think of different characters, each with a specific characterization, and what a dramatic desire for them might be.

Vague desire: A chef who wants to cook something

1. Character: _____ Characterization: _____

Dramatic desire: _____

2. Character: _____ Characterization: _____

Dramatic desire: _____

Vague desire: A scientist who wants to invent something

1. Character: _____ Characterization: _____

Dramatic desire: _____

2. Character: _____ Characterization: _____

Dramatic desire: _____

Vague desire: An explorer who wants to discover something in the jungle

1. Character: _____ Characterization: _____

Dramatic desire: _____

2. Character: _____ Characterization: _____

Dramatic desire: _____

Vague desire: A five-year-old child who wants to help their parent with something

1. Character: _____ Characterization: _____

Dramatic desire: _____

2. Character: _____ Characterization: _____

Dramatic desire: _____

Vague desire: A police officer who wants to arrest criminals

1. Character: _____ Characterization: _____

Dramatic desire: _____

2. Character: _____ Characterization: _____

Dramatic desire: _____

What a character desires affects who that character is and what they do. Without dramatic desires, not much would happen in a story. Remember dramatic desires are those desires that can be completed. Desires give the characters motivation to act in ways that "drive" the story much like the engine in a car enables that car to move.

STAKES

What happens if a character doesn't achieve their desire? What are the consequences of failure?

If Gary is lost in the Go'Gobi desert, his overarching desire will be: to no longer be lost.

His specific – dramatic – desire could be: to get back to his camp before nightfall.

But, what are the stakes for Gary if he does not achieve his dramatic desire? It could be 1. He will die of thirst, or 2. He will spend the night in the bitter cold (the Go'Gobi desert can drop below freezing at night), or 3. He will miss watching his favorite television show.

In order to write a story about Gary you need to know what is at stake if he does not achieve his desire. Stakes are important because they motivate characters to strive to achieve their desire. (Also, can you see how each of the different three stakes given for Gary would create a different kind of story?)

Stakes: What is at risk if a character does not achieve their desire.

Come up with three possible stakes for these examples.

1. A big test is coming up, and Andy really wants to pass it.

What could happen if Andy fails the test?

1. _____

2. _____

3. _____

2. Laura lost a book she borrowed from the library.

What could happen if she can't find the book?

1. _____

2. _____

3. _____

3. A few hours before the wedding, the bride spills juice on her dress.

What could happen if she can't get her dress clean?

1. _____

2. _____

3. _____

4. Jessica wants to talk on the phone to Rhonda, but Jessica's brother won't let her use it.

What could happen if they don't get to talk?

1. _____

2. _____

3. _____

5. Jody needs to get to sleep so she'll be rested for the dance recital in the morning, but she's too nervous.

What could happen if Jody doesn't get enough sleep?

1. _____

2. _____

3. _____

Stakes give reasons and motivations to a character to accomplish something. The bigger and more severe the consequences of failure, the harder the character will work to achieve their desire.

TICKING CLOCK

Characters are also motivated by what we call a "ticking clock."

Sometimes a character only has a certain amount of time to accomplish a task. It is similar to a deadline in that it puts pressure on a character to get to work on their desire <u>now</u>!

Without a ticking clock many desires are never accomplished.

Remember poor Gary, lost in the desert. He has a ticking clock. If he doesn't get water in two days, he'll be dead. That's pretty good motivation for him to get moving and not waste time lounging around getting a suntan.

<u>*Ticking clock: The pressure on a character to accomplish their desire before time runs out*</u>

What is the ticking clock in the following examples?

1. A bomb is about to go off on Monkey Mountain, and Secret Agent Mandy has to get to the evil pirate lair to stop it.

Ticking clock: _____

2. The kids on the canoe are trying to row home, but on the horizon, they spot storm clouds.

Ticking clock: _____

3. Grandma and Grandpa are coming to visit, but the house is a total mess!

Ticking clock: _____

4. Pierre the Painter is trying to finish his masterpiece, but it's getting dark, and he doesn't have any electricity in his home.

Ticking clock: _____

5. The box of ice cream is sitting out on the table and looks delicious, but the weather is getting hotter every second!

Ticking clock: _____

Now that you understand what a ticking clock is, time to create your own. I'll give you a character and a dramatic desire, and you create the ticking clock.

1. Bob wants to see Alaska before he dies.

Ticking clock: Bob is a bug and he has a lifespan of 53 days.

2. Malexander wants to see the new *Monkey Mania* movie in a theater.

Ticking clock: _____

3. Amy wants to tan her skin nice and dark.

Ticking clock: _____

4. Norman wants to make dinner for the hungry crew.

Ticking clock: _____

5. Hailey wants to be the first one to finish writing the test.

Ticking clock: _____

6. Nadia wants to be a kid forever.

Ticking clock: _____

"HEAVE HO!"

Think of a character from a story you like and describe them briefly:

Character: _____ Description: _____

_____

What is this character's desire?

_____

What are the stakes for them?

_____

Is there a ticking clock? What is it?

_____

Think of a character from a story you like and describe them briefly:

Character: _____ Description: _____

_____

What is this character's desire?

_____

What are the stakes for them?

_____

Is there a ticking clock? What is it?

_____

Think of a character from a story you like and describe them briefly:

Character: _____ Description: _____

_____

What is this character's desire?

_____

What are the stakes for them?

_____

Is there a ticking clock? What is it?

_____

RAISE THE ANCHOR AND SET SAIL

Knowing a character's dramatic desire is a great help when writing a story. If you want help starting this story, think of two characters who have conflicting dramatic desires.

_____

_____

_____

_____

_____

_____

_____

_____

_____

_____

_____

_____

_____

_____

_____

_____

_____

_____

_____

_____

_____

_____

_____

_____

_____

CHAPTER AVAST ARGH AYE AYE

"La de da de da de do! Sailin' is a lot to do!" the monkeys sing out as they dance past you and onto the deck, where the one called Monkey Melody is jumping around in the center and scratching out a pleasant tune on the violin. The song is catchy and reminds you of something you'd probably hear at an Irish festival.

"La de da de da de do! Th' music is fer me and you!"

It's Wednesday night – the night where all the monkeys line up beside each other, lift their knees high into the air, stomp their feet, skip around, and dance the jig.

Stomp.

Slide.

Jump.

Clap.

This isn't the first time you've seen them do this, but something about it feels different. It takes you a few minutes, but you start to notice that several monkeys are missing.

"Hey!" you call to Monkey Monica, who is currently spinning in circles next to Monkey Mo Mo.

"Hey you self!" Monkey Monica giggles as she throws her arms up and down in the air.

"La de da de da de do! We no swab th' deck of poo!"

Somehow, the singing gets louder, and you have to raise your voice as much as possible to be heard.

"Where is everyone?" you shout.

"Where who?" Monkey Monica shouts back at you.

"Everyone! Where is everyone?" you ask again.

"Dancing!" Monkey Monica replies as she spins away from you and locks arms with Monkey M, who dances differently than the others and has more of a sway and swagger to his moves.

"Yo! Looks like I still remember how to dance!" you hear him shout confidently.

You grunt with frustration and try to get a better look at the crowd. But – just as you suspected – several monkeys are missing.

"Where is Mini Mate? Or Monkey Martin?" you shout again, but Monkey Monica can't seem to hear you.

Stomp.

Slide.

Jump.

Clap.

"They down below. Rowing," Monkey Mo Mo answers rather sheepishly.

"Down below? Why?" You don't understand. This is the one of the most popular nights and activities of the week.

Monkey Mo Mo lowers his eyes to the floor and stops dancing. You can see his lips move, but you can't hear anything he says because the music and singing are too loud.

"La de da de da de do! Monkey see and monkey do!" the monkeys sing together.

"I can't hear you!" you shout at Monkey Mo Mo.

He looks up at you with fear in his eyes and runs away from you and back to the middle of the dance floor.

Stomp.

Slide.

Jump.

Clap.

"Hey!" you call to him, but he won't look at you.

"If you want them, all the island-liars are down below!" Monkey Monica shouts at you as she slides by.

"Island-liars?" you repeat. "You mean you still haven't seen the island?"

"Never looked again," Monkey Monica giggles. "I know there no island. So why work harder when we can dance and play? Nothing change."

"Yeah," Monkey M chimes in as he glides by you. "Enjoy the party, yo!"

Stomp.

Slide.

Jump.

Clap.

"La de da de da de do! Dancin' fun in wooden shoe!"

As much as you enjoy dancing with monkeys, you're bothered that so many of the ones you know are missing, and it seems strange that Monkey Monica keeps referring to them as "liars," since you saw the island with your own eyes.

You decide you'll have to save your dance moves for another time and head down to the lower decks and see what the other monkeys are up to.

*   *   *

Even though you're deep inside the ship, you can still hear the muffled sound of singing and stomping from above.

You're standing on one of the lower decks – the one with all the oars. Normally, this room is empty on a Wednesday night. But tonight, you find it filled with a few monkeys, sitting on wooden benches and rowing hard with giant oars perfectly in sync with one another.

On the right side sit Mini Mate, Norman Nopants, and Missy Monkey. On the left side sit the extra stinky monkeys: Monkey Martin, Monkey Morgan, and Monkey Morta.

"Heave!" Mini Mate calls out from his position at the front.

"Ho!" the other monkeys answer in unison.

"Heave!" Mini Mate cries again.

"Ho!" they reply.

Every single monkey here is rowing with all their might.

"What's going on?"

"We rowing!" Missy Monkey grunts.

"But why aren't you up there dancing? It's Wednesday."

"We rowin' t' get t' th' island faster!" Mini Mate spits as he speaks. You notice that the hair of all the monkeys is damp with sweat.

"Heave!"

"Ho!"

They've clearly been at this a long time.

"Other monkeys no see," Monkey Morgan grumbles. "We know. We row. We want to go."

"Ha! That rhyme!" Monkey Morta giggles.

"It does, too!" Monkey Morgan grins with pride.

Mini Mate glares.

"Heave!"

"Ho!"

"Heave!"

"Ho!"

"You goin' t' help us, Spat?" Monkey Martin sneers at you. "Or you goin' ta dance with th' ones who no care?"

You hesitate.

You saw the island too, and you do want to get there quicker. Even though the idea of working late on a Wednesday night seems strange to you, you feel yourself filled with a strong desire to reach the magic jelly beans. And so, without another thought, you sit down on a bench on the right side and grab one of the unused oars.

"Good lil' human," Monkey Martin grins. "If we keep rowin', we bound to get thar soon."

"Uh-huh," you agree as you push hard on the oar. It's not easy, but you feel yourself falling into sync with the others.

"Heave!"

"Ho!"

"Heave!"

"<u>Ho</u>!" you shout at the top of your lungs.

EXERCISE #18: STORY ENGINE

As we've learned, every story begins with a problem that causes the characters in the story to take action. This is the Act of Villainy. Then, we learned every story has characters and characters have desires; they want something. Now we are turning to plot, and we will learn that the Act of Villainy and character desires will lead the characters in the story to make choices and to do things. These choices and actions lead other characters to make choices and to act. This goes on and on until the story ends. This series of actions is the plot.

Think of a story like a car. If you want a car to move and take you someplace, it needs an engine. Plot is like a moving car. It's going someplace. But, movement in a story requires what we call a story engine.

Monkey Mary loves banana cream ice cream. Her mother says she will take her out for a cone if she practices playing the piano an hour a day for the next week. What do you think Mary will do?

_____

Why? _____

Ol' Stumpy Humph (a.k.a. Captain Redbeard) couldn't wait for the new Death Ray 8000X. He waited in line at the Super Evil Death Mart three days and nights to make sure he got one the first day it went on sale.

Why did he do this? _____

Make a list of things you want. They can be physical things (a new coconut for coconut football), social things (for your team to win at coconut football), emotional things (your coconut football coach saying, "Good job, monkey mate!"), intellectual things (memorizing all the coconut football statistics for your favorite team), or anything.

1. 587 kilograms of bananas
2. _____
3. _____
4. _____
5. _____
6. _____
7. _____
8. _____
9. _____
10. _____

Take three of these things and list what you would be willing to do in order to get it. Go crazy!

Thing: 587 kilos of bananas

Is worth: cutting the lawn with toe nail clippers, fighting a Class 4 black-scaled Kraken Karen, and eating a moldy pumpkin.

Thing: _____

Is worth: _____

_____

_____

Thing: _____

Is worth: _____

_____

_____

Thing: _____

Is worth: _____

_____

_____

It's not hard to do something if it will get you the thing you want. Actions follow what our heart desires. _Characters are the story engine; characters are the engine of every story._

Kaylee, a four-year-old girl, is visiting the jelly-bean factory store. She wants to try some jelly beans, but the line is really long. How might this cause her to act?

1. She will run behind the counter, punch the cashier in the knees, and grab a handful of jelly beans.

2. She will stand in the long line, waiting her turn patiently, because she really, really wants to try a jelly bean.

3. She will try to convince the kids in front that she is sick and dying and needs to get a jelly bean quickly before it's too late.

4. She will shout fire to make everyone leave the line, and then step up to the front.

5. _____

6. _____

7. _____

Monkey M has no memories and really wants to find out who he is and where he is from.

What are two things this desire would lead him to do?

1. _____

2. _____

Monkey Monica wants to take a nap, and Captain Yogger says she can as soon as all the chores get finished.

What are two things that this desire would lead her to do?

1. _____

2. _____

Squeaky is a mouse who wants to get a piece of cheese sitting on the dining room table. Unfortunately, Katlynn McGillikitty – the family cat – is always watching.

What are two things that this desire would lead Squeaky to do?

1. _____

2. _____

Orangutan Olga's twin sister Orva was supposed to help wash the ship, but when it was time to start, Orva was nowhere to be found. Olga really doesn't want to be the only one washing the boat.

What are two things that this desire would lead her to do?

1. _____

2. _____

ACTIONS REVEAL DESIRES

Desires are sneaky things. We don't always know what another person's desires are. Sometimes we don't even know what we desire. One way to discover what a character wants is to look at their actions.

Read the following characters and actions. What do their actions reveal about what they want?

1. Ol' Blue, an old barn cat, is circling around the legs of her owner, purring loudly. She wants:

_____

2. Monte, a circus monkey with a fear of heights, is sweating like crazy as he balances on the tight rope. He wants:

_____

3. Mabel, the proud princess of the Brintish Isles, refuses to marry the Kanadien prince. She wants:

_____

4. Hoppy, the hungry bunny, is hopping around the garden. He wants:

_____

5. Monkey Mitch and Monkey Mervin snuck away from the dance to go take a banana break. They want:

_____

Come up with three different desires for each example that could lead to the following actions:

1. A criminal breaks into a bank and steals a bunch of money.

Desire: _____

Desire: _____

Desire: _____

2. A father and son go fishing together. Whenever they catch a fish, they release it from the hook, kiss it, and let it go.

Desire: _____

Desire: _____

Desire: _____

3. A young woman buys a plane ticket to India, but when the day for the flight comes, she decides not to go.

Desire: _____

Desire: _____

Desire: _____

4. Every Monday night, a child goes to the store and buys a board game.

Desire: _____

Desire: _____

Desire: _____

CONFLICTING DESIRES

Many times we have multiple desires. Mini Mate *wants* to get to the island, but he doesn't *want* to wait. So that makes him *want* to work hard to get there faster. But he's exhausted and *wants* to rest. These conflicting desires will rumble around inside him and force him to make a choice between them. What will he do?

1. Teri, a 14-year-old big sister, wants her little sister Sarah to leave her alone so she can study, but she also wants to be a good sister and help Sarah with her work.

What's something that these desires could cause her to do?

_____

_____

What's something else these desires could cause her to do?

_____

_____

2. Mariah, a 13-year-old monkey who is allergic to gluten but loves desserts, is at a birthday party where all of her friends are eating cake:

What could that desire cause her to do?

_____

_____

What's something else which that desire could cause her to do?

_____

_____

3. Toby and Alora, a brother and sister, want to go to the beach with their family, but they also want to go to their best friend's birthday party on a pirate ship.

What could these desires cause them to do?

_____

_____

What's something else that these desires could cause them to do?

_____

_____

4. The old farmer is sick and wants to get better so he can go to work, but he also wants to stay away from hospitals and doctors.

What could these desires cause him to do?

_____

_____

What's something else that these desires could cause him to do?

_____

_____

5. Monkey Mo Mo is scared of a lot of things and wants to be safe at all costs, but he also wants to go on adventures and see interesting and exciting new places.

What could these desires cause him to do?

_____

_____

What's something else these desires could cause him to do?

_____

_____

CHOICES

As the above exercise shows, when a character has conflicting desires it requires them to make difficult choices.

Sometimes the choice is between multiple bad things. Think of Monkey Mariah with the gluten allergy at the birthday party. Does she eat the cake and get sick, or does she not eat any cake and feel out of place with her friends?

Her choice will be based on what she considers the lesser of two evils.

If you had to choose between the following two things which one would you choose?

One bad thing   OR   Another bad thing

Circle one:

1. Being punched on the arm OR being punched on the leg?

2. Falling into a big pit OR being launched into the sky?

3. Getting lost in a forest overnight OR getting lost in a city overnight?

4. Never getting to eat ice cream again OR never getting to eat cookies?

Try to create your own:

5. _____ OR _____?

6. _____ OR _____?

7. _____ OR _____?

8. _____ OR _____?

Other times we have the opposite problem. We have to make a choice between two good things. Here we make the choice based on what we consider the greater of two goods:

One good thing   OR   Another good thing

Circle one:

1. Never having to go to school again OR never having to sleep again?

2. Living on a beautiful, tropical island OR living on a cool pirate ship?

3. Exploring outer space OR exploring the deep ocean?

4. Having the ability to run really fast OR having the ability to swim really fast

Try to create your own:

5. _____ OR _____?

6. _____ OR _____?

7. _____ OR _____?

8. _____ OR _____?

CONFLICT

One of the best types of fuel for any story engine is conflict. Conflict is born when two characters have conflicting desires.

Malina lived on Monkey Mountain with her brother Moory. She wants to go out for banana pizza, but Moory hates pizza and wants to go out for banana burgers.

Come up with three possible ways Moory could react to this situation.

1. _____

_____

2. _____

_____

3. _____

_____

220

Pick one of these, and say that's what Moory actually did.

Now, come up with three possible ways Malina could respond to her brother's action.

1. _____

_____

2. _____

_____

3. _____

_____

Monkey Melody started to sing one night on the deck, but Monkey Martin wanted to try and get some sleep and couldn't with all the noise.

Come up with three possible ways Monkey Martin could react to the singing.

1. _____

_____

2. _____

_____

3. _____

_____

Pick one of these, and say that's what Monkey Martin did.

Come up with three possible ways Monkey Melody could respond.

1. _____

_____

2. _____

_____

3. _____

_____

Captain Yogger wanted to teach Monkey Mo Mo how to swim, but Monkey Mo Mo was too scared and didn't want to do it.

Come up with three possible ways Captain Yogger could help Monkey Mo Mo learn to swim.

1. _____

_____

2. _____

_____

3. _____

_____

Pick one of these, and say that's what Captain Yogger did.

Come up with three possible ways Monkey Mo Mo could respond.

1. _____

_____

2. _____

_____

3. _____

_____

Pick one of these, and say that's what Monkey Mo Mo did.

Come up with three possible ways Captain Yogger could respond.

1. _____

_____

2. _____

_____

3. _____

_____

Characters drive the story. They are the story engine.

As a story creator you have the job of getting to know your characters so that you will know how they will act in the story. The more they know about their character, the easier it is to see what choices they will make.

Likewise, when you read a story you come to know who a character is based on the actions and choices they make. If you see Monkey Martin rush in and steal a jelly bean from Captain Yogger, you know that he *wants* to have a jelly bean so much that he is willing to face all the conflict that will come when Captain Yogger discovers one of his beans was stolen.

Now you understand what a story engine is, it's time to examine all the different roles the individual characters fulfill.

SCRATCH YER NOGGIN'

How well do you remember what you've learned?

1. To be significant is to be something worthy of _____

2. What are some ways you could make a piece of bubble gum significant?

_____   _____

_____   _____

_____   _____

3. What explains why a character is afraid of spiders? _____

4. _____ describe things and give details of who or what a character is.

5. What are some things that characterizations can tell you about a character?

_____   _____

_____   _____

_____   _____

6. Characterizations, like all things in story, are something you should make as _____ as possible.

7. The process of creating a character is called: _____

8. Give the following characters a new last names based on the theme.

Hailey: Alex:

Comedy: Hailey _____   Comedy: Alex _____

Horror: Hailey _____   Horror: Alex _____

Romance: Hailey _____   Romance: Alex _____

Action: Hailey _____   Action: Alex _____

9. What is the greatest source of mystery in a story? _____

10. What do we call the technique a storyteller uses to give hints about a mystery?

_____

INTRO TO CHARACTER FUNCTIONS

A character is an actor in a story. A character may be a person, an animal, a worldling, a significant object, or any number of things. Characters fulfill different functions (or established roles). Though a story will usually have many different characters, there are only a few primary functions.

The role – or function – a character plays in a story is determined by who they are (characterizations), what they want (desires), the choices they make (story engine), and the actions they take (plot).

A character may fulfill different functions at different points of the story, and take on a variety of roles when seen from different points of view.

Sound confusing? It ought to, because it is.

This is complex, so we are going to keep the definitions of each function simple and use simple stories to show you how to identify the different character functions.

CHAPTER AVAST ARGH AYE AYE AYE

It's late at night – and far past the time you normally fall asleep – but you're up on the top deck doing the night watch.

"What a beautiful night!" you say to yourself. So far, you've seen nothing but dark, crashing waves. And even though not a lot has happened – and you're incredibly tired – you feel excited about the responsibility you've been entrusted with. Captain Yogger believes in you and considers you one of his crew. Considering you're the only human on board – aside from the captain – you feel really good about being here.

"I hope I do a good job," you say with a yawn as you try not to think about all the other monkeys wrapped up in their beds and sleeping peacefully.

As much as you want to stay awake, sleepiness starts to creep in, and you shake your head around a few times to try and refocus.

Just when you start to think this might be more difficult than you expected, you hear the howling laughter of Monkey Martin, Monkey Morgan, and Monkey Morta coming from the front of the ship.

"Har har!"

"Yeah! Har har!" echoes Monkey Morta.

"Dumb humans. This be good," Monkey Morgan claps his hands together.

You know those three have been ordered to sleep on the top deck due to their gross smell, but you can't understand why they'd still be awake – especially at this late hour. Though you are worried about what mischief they might be getting into this time, you know it's part of your job tonight, so you stride across the deck to where they're supposed to be sleeping.

"What are you guys doing up?" you ask as you cover your nose; the fresh air helps the stinky smell, but just barely.

"None of yer business, Spat," Monkey Martin sneers.

But at the exact same time, Monkey Morta answers, "Watchin' the monster!"

You can't help but smile.

"Monster, huh?" You think these monkeys are just imagining things, but then, all at once, you hear a loud, wailing screech.

"What was that?" you ask nervously.

"A kraken!" Monkey Morgan says with a wry smile. "I bet ye twenty coins he sink them all in under a minute!"

"Me too!" Monkey Morta agrees happily.

"Aye. Bet you're right," Monkey Martin chuckles. "They's just Kanadiens."

You look out at the ocean but don't see any sign of a monster. You do, however, notice there's another ship in the distance. You grab your night-watch telescope to try to get a good look at the flag they're flying, and recognize it as what would be a Canadian flag in your world, but colored blue instead of red.

"I don't see anything but a ship. . ." you start to say, when all of a sudden, a large, dark green beast rises out of the sea.

You can hardly believe your eyes; the monster is at least 30 times larger than the other ship and looks like a giant, scaled octopus with several thrashing, green tentacles and a wide mouth full of razor-sharp teeth, which it opens to let out another high-pitched howl.

"Hi, kraken!" Monkey Morta giggles. "Make us money!"

You can faintly hear a chorus of cries and screams for help from the people on the ship as they wave their arms in the air and try to fire shots at the monster, but it's clear to you that unless they get help soon, there's not much hope for them.

You look through the telescope again and see that one of the people on the ship – a man with long, golden hair – rips off his shirt and exposes his rippling muscles.

"Meataloaf ready to fight!" he screams at the top of his lungs; his words echo off the water and ring all the way to your ears. You watch with excitement as he leaps off the boat and lands on the kraken.

Everyone on the boat cheers and chants his name as he scales up the beast.

"Whoa! That guy looks tough!" you cry with excitement.

"I bet he fall off," Monkey Morta grunts.

"Definitely fall off. I bet that, too!" Monkey Morgan agrees.

You find it strange how they keep agreeing on the same bets and wonder if the monkeys understand how betting actually works.

You watch amazed as the man who calls himself Meataloaf rides on the back of the kraken, punching it as hard as he can over and over.

The kraken lets out a howl, and you start to think this guy might actually stand a chance, when all of a sudden – in one swift motion – the kraken lifts one of its tentacles and easily slaps the man off its back and straight up into the air.

The look of shock on his face fills you with fear as he tumbles through the air and is swallowed whole by the kraken in one fierce gulp. . .

EXERCISE #19: PRINCESS AND VILLAIN

VILLAIN

VILLAIN: a character/thing that is on the side of the Act of Villainy. Villains are characters whose function is to support the Act of Villainy that the Hero is trying to resolve.

The Villain can be the cause of the AoV, but not always. Sometimes, they just support or take advantage of it. Villains see the AoV as a good thing.

Identify the Villain in the following sentences.

1. Grandpa refused to take the kids to the amusement park that day.

     Identify the Villain: _____

2. All the monkey mates loved to dance and were looking forward to the party, but Monkey Muse wasn't feeling very musical that night and refused to sing.

     Identify the Villain: _____

3. A snake slithered past the kids and was about to bite Steve, when a badger jumped out and caught it.

     Identify the Villain: _____

4. The kids were sad to discover that the ice cream store was closed today, despite the sign that said it was open 24 hours a day.

     Identify the Villain: _____

5. Because we didn't have the proper permits to camp in the national park, the police officer forced my family to leave.

     Identify the Villain: _____

Number 5 was a bit trickier, right? To the family, the police officer was the Villain. But to the police officer, the family was the Villain. The family could also see the people who created the National Park rule as the Villain. Who the Villain is depends on what point of view you take.

A story can have any number of Villains, big and small. In all cases, the Villain(s) will support some AoV in the story. Oftentimes, in simple stories, there is one main Villain, who is the character who provides the most support to the primary AoV in the story. There may also be minor Villains who support the AoV in smaller ways.

List ten Villains from stories you know, and describe how they were on the side of the AoV:

Example:

Wicked stepmother in Monkeyella – wants to keep Monkeyella her servant

1. _____   6. _____
2. _____   7. _____
3. _____   8. _____
4. _____   9. _____
5. _____   10. _____

PRINCESS

PRINCESS: a character/thing being fought over.

Is the Princess an actual princess? Almost never.

Does the Princess have to be a female? No.

Is the Princess a person or character? Not always.

The Princess can be anything that is desired. It can be a person, a tree in your yard, your dog, your childhood home, an actual princess, bananas, magic jelly beans, your brother or sister, the ozone layer, coral reefs, anything. The Princess performs the <u>function</u> in the story of being the character or thing that is desired and/or needs to be saved.

Often the Act of Villainy has harmed or threatens to harm the Princess. The Villain may have captured her or is trying to capture her. It's common for the Princess to be in danger. This causes the characters who desire her to take actions to rescue or protect her.

1. A group of bullies were pushing Sammy around on the playground, but they stopped when Danica saw and called the teacher.

     Identify the Princess: _____

2. The kids were having fun at the park, but it started to rain, and they weren't allowed to play outside anymore.

     Identify the Princess: _____

3. As long as krakens roam the seas, no ship is safe.

     Identify the Princess: _____

4. I wanted to make myself some microwave popcorn, but I can't because there is no microwave, electricity, or popcorn on the ship.

     Identify the Princess: _____

5. We monkey mates really want to eat a banana, but can't, because we know that bananas make us smell bad.

    Identify the Princess: _____

Sometimes, as in the above examples, there is only one possible Princess. But, there are some situations when there can be many different Princesses.

Imagine this Act of Villainy: a dangerous forest fire has started on the mainland!

Identify some possible Princesses who might be in danger.

1. Nearby houses
2. Trees
3. _____
4. _____
5. _____

6. _____
7. _____
8. _____
9. _____
10. _____

The Princess in this example could be many things. The one you choose to focus on will define what story you're telling. If you want to tell a story about animals, then you will want to focus the story on how the fire has harmed the forest animals. What if your story is about a small town where a lumber mill is the primary employer?

Then the Princess will probably be _____

Now, here is a list of possible Villains for the forest fire. Draw a circle around the one you think is the main Villain of the story of the forest fire.

                    The wind / The fire / The boy that started the fire

Is it the boy who started the fire? He created the Act of Villainy, but is he the primary Villain of the story? Yes or no? Why? _____

If the boy was arrested, would this do anything to resolve the main problem of the story?

_____

Or is the Villain the fire? Yes or no? Why?

_____

What about the wind?

_____

Can you think of 4 characters and/or things that could resolve – liquidate – the Act of Villainy?

1. _____   3. _____

2. _____   4. _____

Identify a possible Princess and Villain in the following sentences:

1. Monkey Morgan jumped down onto the table and stole my sandwich.

Princess: _____ Villain: _____

2. Homework is taking up all Benjamin's time and keeping him from being able to play the new video game he bought.

Princess: _____ Villain: _____

3. When the dog ran up the stairs it woke me up!

Princess: _____ Villain: _____

4. When Monkey Mo Mo got curious and climbed up a tree he couldn't climb down, Mini Mate climbed up and rescued him.

Princess: _____ Villain: _____

5. I ate too many nachos for lunch and now I feel sick.

Princess: _____ Villain: _____

The following is a list of Villains. Imagine a Princess this Villain might want to harm or take captive.

1. Villain: A mean brother   Princess: _____

2. Villain: A grumpy story teacher Princess: _____

3. Villain: A big storm   Princess: _____

4. Villain: A monster   Princess: _____

5. Villain: An annoying song   Princess: _____

6. Villain: A school bully   Princess: _____

Do the same exercise again, only this time I will give you the Princesses. Come up with your own Villain who would want to harm or try to take the Princess captive.

1. Princess: A candy store   Possible Villain: _____

2. Princess: A bank   Possible Villain: _____

3. Princess: A baby bird   Possible Villain: _____

4. Princess: A cute baby monkey   Possible Villain: _____

5. Princess: A content family   Possible Villain: _____

6. Princess: A bucket of jelly beans   Possible Villain: _____

On the left, make your own list of Villains, and on the right, a list of Princesses.

1. _____   1. _____
2. _____   2. _____
3. _____   3. _____
4. _____   4. _____
5. _____   5. _____
6. _____   6. _____
7. _____   7. _____
8. _____   8. _____
9. _____   9. _____
10. _____   10. _____

Just for fun, see if you can draw a line connecting any of the Princesses on your list with any of the Villains. Do you have the beginning of a story? Write a few lines about it.

_____

_____

_____

_____

Connect a different Villain to a different Princess. Write a few lines about it.

_____

_____

_____

_____

CHAPTER AVAST AYE AVAST

You spin on your heels and run straight toward the Captain's cabin; if the fight between Meataloaf and the kraken is any indication, you don't think those Kanadiens have long.

"Spat! Don't ye dare wake LeFossa an' spoil th' fun!" Monkey Martin shouts at you, but you don't listen; you've been given a job to report if anything happens during the night, and you would never forgive yourself if you sat idly by and let those poor souls on the ship get destroyed.

"We have a problem!" you practically scream the words as you throw open Captain Yogger's door.

As soon as you enter, Captain Yogger sits straight up in his bed and screams at the top of his lungs.

"AHHHHH!"

His scream startles you so bad that you stumble back and scream in response.

"Ahhh!"

"AHHH!"

"Ahh!"

The two of you stare at one another and alternate panicked screams until – after the longest minute of your life – Captain Yogger finally calms down.

"What are ye thinkin', bustin' in like that! Ye nearly gave me a heart-stop!" he growls.

"I – uh," you stammer as you try to catch your breath, "There's a . . . ship out on the sea and . . ."

"Uh-huh. A ship. Go on," Captain Yogger insists.

"There's a . . . a . . ."

"Go on! Get it out!"

". . . a kraken!" you finally manage to speak the word.

Captain Yogger stares at you blankly for a few seconds, then leaps out of his bed and hastily gets dressed.

"Sink me! A kraken, ye say? Good . . . great! It bein' too long. Fetch me First Mate Manfred. I has work t' do!"

EXERCISE #20: DISPATCH AND HERO

HERO

Hero: a character/thing that liquidates the Act of Villainy.

Every single story has a Hero, because the Act of Villainy that births a story must be liquidated (resolved) before the story can end. The character who liquidates the AoV will, by this definition, be the Hero of the story. Often, this is the main character, and the story is about this character seeking to eliminate the AoV. But it can be anyone, even a minor character.

This way of describing the Hero is different from the way most other kraken-riding, storytelling pirates describe it. There isn't much agreement about Heroes among pirates, so you'll have to just trust Captain Yogger as long as you're on this ship. The way he sees it, the Hero fulfills the <u>function</u> in the story of the character who liquidates the Act of Villainy.

Using the Act of Villainy of the forest fire, make a list of six possible Heroes who could defeat it. Keep in mind that it's usually important for the Princess to be someone or something the Hero cares about, otherwise the Hero will have no reason to work to rescue it. (Be creative: finding six will be hard.)

1. _____   4. _____

2. _____   5. _____

3. _____   6. _____

THREE KINDS OF HEROES

There are three different types of Heroes, and it's important to understand the difference between them.

1. A SEEKER HERO

A Seeker Hero is someone who resolves an AoV that affects someone else. A doctor saving the life of a patient is a great example of a Seeker Hero, as are police officers, teachers, and sail boat builders. The doctor isn't sick (the AoV is not harming them), but when they heal someone, they are the Hero of the story.

Think of six problems you have faced in your life that you knew you could not solve. Then identify the Seeker Hero who did, in fact, solve the problem for you.

1. Problem: _____   Seeker Hero: _____

2. Problem: _____   Seeker Hero: _____

3. Problem: _____   Seeker Hero: _____

4. Problem: _____   Seeker Hero: _____

5. Problem: _____   Seeker Hero: _____

6. Problem: _____   Seeker Hero: _____

2. A VICTIM HERO

A Victim Hero is someone who resolves a problem that directly affects them. This could be a child who is lost and, all by themselves, finds their way home. It could be a person who, eating alone, starts to choke and has to find a way to clear their throat. You are being a Victim Hero when you study for a test, take it, and pass. You are even a Victim Hero when you're hungry, and you make yourself a sandwich for lunch.

Think of six problems you have faced in your life that you solved. In these situations you were a Victim Hero.

1. Problem: _____

2. Problem: _____

3. Problem: _____

4. Problem: _____

5. Problem: _____

6. Problem: _____

3. FALSE HERO

A False Hero is someone who appears to be the Hero of the story, but, in the end, they are not the person who liquidates the Act of Villainy. They may act like the Hero. They may care about the Princess. They may be a good character who does everything they can to defeat the Villain. They could be strong, capable, and want to be the Hero. But if – for whatever reason – they are not the one to liquidate the AoV, then, by Captain Yogger's definition, they are not the Hero.

Think of six problems you thought you could solve, but in the end couldn't. These could be problems you faced personally, or ones someone else struggled with, but they must be problems that you were not able to deal with. Then, identify the Hero who did resolve them.

1. Problem: _____ Hero: _____

2. Problem: _____ Hero: _____

3. Problem: _____ Hero: _____

4. Problem: _____ Hero: _____

5. Problem: _____ Hero: _____

6. Problem: _____ Hero: _____

Read the following very short stories and try to determine what type of Hero is in each one. Circle the type of Hero these sentences describe:

1. A group of animal haters takes a dog and throws her into a big hole. The dog spends all night digging, and eventually, she makes a way out to freedom.

Identify the Hero: Seeker / Victim / False

2. A giant kraken is attacking Eastern Osia, and a team of crime-fighting pirates swoop in to defeat the monster and save the day.

Identify the Hero: Seeker / Victim / False

3. A doctor trips walking down the stairs and breaks his arm. He tries to fix it, but is unable.

Identify the Hero: Seeker / Victim / False

4. When a winter snowstorm hits Port Burro, a small fishing town, a search-and-rescue helicopter pilot braves the cold in order to bring blankets to the people there.

Identify the Hero: Seeker / Victim / False

5. A scientist promises he will come up with a cure for all disease, but before he can perfect his formula, someone else beats him to it.

Identify the Hero: Seeker / Victim / False

6. An amusement park loses power and a child is stuck on a roller coaster. After two hours he is able to muster the courage to climb down.

Identify the Hero: Seeker / Victim / False

7. Monkey Marshal promised that if he was elected monkey monarch, he would abolish all bad smells from Monkey Mountain. But after he was voted to be their new monarch, he just hoarded bananas and lay in a hammock all day.

Identify the Hero: Seeker / Victim / False

Take a look at the following AoV sentences and come up with an example of each of the three types of Hero who could be in that story. I'll do the first one for you.

1. A town is invaded by an evil alien.

    Seeker: Mike McOliver, a military commando, parachutes in and fights the alien in hand-to-tentacle combat, emerging victorious after three days.

    Victim: Old 97-year-old Melvin McKrakenson (a.k.a. Uncle Crakky), born and raised in the town, gets out of his rocking chair, hobbles over to the alien and sneezes on it. The alien isn't used to human sicknesses, and dies three days later.

    False: Marky McBanana, the socially-savvy, beloved mayor who tries to make peace but fails, ends up being shot with a freeze gun.

2. After the ship they were on crashed, the passengers were shipwrecked on an island.

    Seeker: _____

    _____

    Victim: _____

    _____

    False: _____

    _____

3. The cell phone fell into the toilet.

    Seeker: _____

    _____

    Victim: _____

    _____

    False: _____

    _____

4. Santa Clause got stuck in a chimney.

    Seeker: _____

    _____

    Victim: _____

    _____

    False: _____

    _____

5. Ketchup spilled on Monkey Morgan's favorite whale t-shirt.

Seeker: _____

_____

Victim: _____

_____

False: _____

_____

6. Slavers are kidnapping monkeys and Monkey Marshal, the newly anointed monkey monarch, is doing nothing to protect the monkeys of Monkey Mountain.

Seeker: _____

_____

Victim: _____

_____

False: _____

_____

Identify 8 Seeker Heroes from stories you know.

1. _____   5. _____

2. _____   6. _____

3. _____   7. _____

4. _____   8. _____

Name 8 Victim Heroes from stories you know.

1. _____   5. _____

2. _____   6. _____

3. _____   7. _____

4. _____   8. _____

List 8 False Heroes from stories you know.

1. _____   5. _____

2. _____   6. _____

3. _____   7. _____

4. _____   8. _____

DISPATCHER

Before a Hero can take action to liquidate an Act of Villainy, they need to know there is a problem to solve.

Therefore, Heroes need to be dispatched; they need to be sent into the story. The character who has the <u>function</u> of informing the Hero there is a problem in the story is named the Dispatcher.

<u>*DISPATCHER: a character/thing that informs the Hero that there is a problem to be solved.*</u>

Imagine a crime has been committed. Someone (the Dispatcher) needs to notify the police of the crime before the police can do anything about it. In real life, dispatch is so crucial that most countries have a special phone number dedicated for it, like 9-1-1.

Describe who/what is the Dispatcher in the following sentences:

1. After the robber left the bank with their bags full of banana bucks, one of the tellers called the police. _____

2. When the evil pirate secretly stole a sword from the sword maker, his daughter told the apprentice to go and get it back! _____

3. The clown couldn't believe his eyes when he saw the newspaper that morning; the headline read: "The circus is going bankrupt!" _____

4. Bobby looked at the thermometer, and when he saw the temperature he rushed outside and saw his snowman was melting! _____

5. From the feeling in her stomach, the girl could tell she was hungry. So after school she went to the store to buy a candy bar. _____

A Dispatcher can be a character who alerts another character(s) to the fact there is a problem. They connect characters to the Act of Villainy.

The moment in the story when a character steps up and decides to become actively involved in combating the AoV is called "The Dispatch."

In the following sentences, identify the Hero and the Dispatcher, and write why.

1. The cries for help from inside the cave led the little girl to run home and tell her father, who came and found a man with a broken leg, unable to get out.

> Hero: <u>The father</u>
>
> Dispatcher: <u>The little girl</u>
>
> Why? <u>If the little girl did not tell her father (the Hero), he would have never known there was someone in trouble crying for help.</u>

2. Alfonso saw some real bad banditos robbing a bank. He called the police, and they arrived in minutes to stop the robbery.

    Hero: _____

    Dispatcher: _____

    Why? _____

    _____

3. Monkey Mo Mo got stuck once again in a tree and cried and cried until our neighbor got so irritated by the noise she told her husband to go get a ladder and rescue him, and so he did.

    Hero: _____

    Dispatcher: _____

    Why? _____

    _____

4. A man was planning to mow the lawn first thing in the morning, but when he woke up to the sound of a lawnmower and went outside, he saw his wife doing his job. When he asked her why she did it, she said she saw it on his to-do list, and decided to help him with all the chores he had to do that day.

    Hero: _____

    Dispatcher: _____

    Why? _____

    _____

5. The monkeys were smelly and rejected by their own kind, but after they cried out to Captain Yogger for help, he took them in and allowed them to live with him on his ship. (This is a tricky one. Ask the question: who notified the Hero that there was a problem?)

    Hero: _____

    Dispatcher: _____

    Why? _____

    _____

6. Malachi, the young knight, who, after reading about the king's daughter being kidnapped on Monkeyfacebook, went forth and rescued the Princess Moya from an evil ogre.

    Hero: _____

    Dispatcher: _____

    Why? _____

    _____

Create a Dispatcher who connects the Hero to the AoV in these examples.

Example: While police officer Maddy is off duty talking on the phone to her mom, a criminal is breaking Into her neighbor's house across the street.
Who could be a Dispatcher in this story? One possible option: Her neighbor who screams, "Help Maddy," out the window. Maddy hangs up the phone and punches the robber in the face and takes them to jail.

1. Mabel, swimming in the ocean, does not see a deadly shark circling her. Unfortunately, neither do the coast guard who are watching the championship FICA game in their office.
Who could be a Dispatcher in this story? _____

_____

_____

2. Marley and Marybeth discover there is no milk in the fridge, but their dad already left for the grocery store and doesn't know he should buy milk.
Who could be a Dispatcher in this story? _____

_____

_____

3. A gross, nasty rat is chewing holes into everything, but the family cat is sleeping in the sun.
Who could be a Dispatcher in this story? _____

_____

_____

4. At Camp Kidsaloo, several children have gotten lost, but no one at camp knows they're gone.
Who could be a Dispatcher in this story? _____

_____

_____

Name 8 Dispatchers from stories you know.

1. _____   5. _____

2. _____   6. _____

3. _____   7. _____

4. _____   8. _____

CHAPTER AVAST AVAST

Waking the first mate is not nearly so traumatic, and once you explain the nature of the situation, he wastes no time in grabbing a large, leather-bound volume from his bookshelf and rushing out the door with you.

As you return to the front of the ship, you see Captain Yogger doing the splits and wiggling around on the ground in what you assume must be some type of vigorous stretching.

"Thanks o'lot, Spat," Monkey Martin grumbles under his breath as you approach.

"It okay. New bet," Monkey Morgan announces. "I bet you . . . LeFossa beats the kraken!"

"I take that action," Monkey Martin agrees.

"Ya, ya! LeFossa beat kraken! You on!" Monkey Morta squirms with delight.

If there was any question before, you're now convinced that these monkeys have no idea how betting works.

"What we lookin' at this time, Manny?" Captain Yogger asks First Mate Manfred, who's currently flipping through the giant tome.

In the time since you left, it seems the kraken has managed to pick up the ship with one of its tentacles and is swinging it around in the air. You aren't sure what Captain Yogger could possibly do now to save them now.

"Class 2, scaled, Kraken Kyle. Mild temperament. Like all Kyles, this one is sensitive to prodding between the scales. Should be no problem," First Mate Manfred states confidently as he shows Captain Yogger a page from the book.

Your heart skips a beat when he says "mild temperament." You hope you never see one that's "severe."

Captain Yogger nods, does one last arm stretch, then climbs up onto the railing.

"Pay attention, me hearties!" he shouts as he balances precariously on the edge and tries to strike a pose. "This be th' moment ye see yer captain bring down a –" Before he can finish speaking, the ship hits a large wave created by the kraken and Captain Yogger slips off the railing and tumbles headlong into the sea.

"Captain!" you cry out as you run to the railing to see if he survived the fall.

You search and search but don't see him anywhere.

"Thar! LeFossa over thar!" Monkey Morta points to the kraken.

You look up and – sure enough – Captain Yogger has somehow managed to spin his peg legs together like some sort of propeller and is rapidly shooting across the water toward the kraken. As soon as he gets close, Captain Yogger launches out of the water like a dolphin and grabs hold of the back of the kraken.

The kraken hisses and screeches as the captain stands on its back and starts to poke and prod it with his legs while dancing around in a circle.

"Yo ho ho!" he cheers and waves his hat in the air.

The kraken lets out another cry and all at once drops the captured Kanadien ship back down to the sea. It then lifts its tentacles into the air like it did when it swallowed Meataloaf. You squint your eyes and brace yourself for the worst, when – much to your surprise – the kraken's tentacles fall limply to the side.

"It's dying!" you can hardly believe it. "It's working!"

"Of course it's working," First Mate Manfred says, "that's Captain Yogger LeFossa. He's spent his life studying for moments like this."

You watch with excitement as the kraken sinks lower and lower into the ocean.

"KRRRRRRRAAAAAAAAAAAAAAAAAAAAAAAAaaaaaaaaaaaaaa!" Its high-pitched screams rip across the water and pierce your ears. You cover them and shut your eyes.

"Krrrraaaaaaaaaa!"

The screaming is weaker now, and when it finally stops, you open your eyes and see that the kraken has become significantly smaller. A few seconds ago, it was a fearsome, dangerous monster, but now, it's shrinking rather rapidly and transforming into a bright yellow, glowing light.

It shrinks and shrinks until there seems to be nothing left; Captain Yogger is now treading water next to the Kanadien ship, and – with one hand – pulls the unconscious, golden-haired man named Meataloaf out of the sea.

"He's alive," you whisper under your breath.

As Captain Yogger starts to swim over to the Kanadien ship – with Meataloaf in tow – a beautiful, white whale appears next to them both. The whale dives away and swims far off to sea until it's gone.

You gasp.

"Did he just turn the kraken into a whale?" you ask no one in particular.

It seems fitting, then, that no one answers.

You watch with new-found respect as Captain Yogger climbs aboard the Kanadien ship.

EXERCISE #21: DONOR AND MAGICAL AGENT

In order to defeat Villains and liquidate Acts of Villainy, a Hero needs a specific thing that is able to help resolve the Act of Villainy.

Captain Yogger calls these things Magical Agents. They remind him of magical jelly beans.

If the Hero doesn't have the appropriate Magical Agent, then they need to acquire it. The Donor fulfills the <u>function</u> in the story of providing the Hero with the Magical Agent they need.

The DONOR: a character/thing that connects the Hero to the Magical Agent.

Just like the Dispatcher connects the Hero to the AoV, the Donor connects the Hero to the Magical Agent.

The MAGICAL AGENT: a character/thing that is needed to liquidate (solve) the Act of Villainy.

The Magical Agent fulfills the <u>function</u> of being the thing that the Hero uses to defeat the Villain and/or liquidate the Act of Villainy.

It could be something tangible, like a weapon, or a character; or something you can't touch, like a skill, wisdom, or some secret knowledge. It could be almost anything. But, whatever it is, it is necessary to defeat the VillainVillain and/or solve the AoV. If the HeroHero tries to fight the VillainVillain without the proper MMagical AAgent, they will lose.

Create three different Donors that connect the Hero to the Magical Agent in the following sentences. Remember, it can be a person, knowledge, a place, or even another item.

1. No matter how hard Henry Hosogawa tried, he was unable to defeat the fire dragon.
    Magical Agent: A sword of ice
    Donor: Mary McGillicutty, his third cousin who lived in Icyland
    Donor: A how-to video called "Making Weapons with Liquid Nitrogen and Water"
    Donor: The Super-Evil Death Mart
2. Horace Henpecked, the guitar player, was about to perform a concert, but found two of his guitar strings were broken!

    Magical Agent: New guitar strings

    Donor: _____

    Donor: _____

    Donor: _____

3. As the children neared the end of the book, they realized the last pages were missing.

    Magical Agent: The missing pages

    Donor: _____

    Donor: _____

    Donor: _____

4. Huck Finn wanted to travel down the river, but he had nothing to float on.

Magical Agent: A raft

Donor: _____

Donor: _____

Donor: _____

5.Tom wasn't allowed to play until the fence was painted.

Magical Agent: Paint

Donor: _____

Donor: _____

Donor: _____

Let's do this again, only this time, I'll give you the Donor and you tell me what would be a good Magical Agent to enable the Hero liquidate the AoV.

1. Harry wanted to pass the test in order to become a wizard.

Donor: A wizard teacher

Magical Agent: _____

Magical Agent: _____

Magical Agent: _____

2. Doctor Mona Mayberry needed to find a treatment for Mack, a patient who was sick with a mysterious virus.

Donor: The internet

Magical Agent: _____

Magical Agent: _____

Magical Agent: _____

3. Marisol, a truck driver, could hardly stay awake after a long night of driving, and she still had 328 miles to her destination in Marysville.

Donor: The Caffeinated Banana Bean Cafe

Magical Agent: _____

Magical Agent: _____

Magical Agent: _____

4. Margaux dropped her glasses, and when she picked them up, there was a big scratch!

    Donor: A glasses store

    Magical Agent: _____

    Magical Agent: _____

    Magical Agent: _____

5. Maximus, a seven-year-old boy, couldn't sleep because he was sure there was a monster in the dark corner.

    Donor: A parent

    Magical Agent: _____

    Magical Agent: _____

    Magical Agent: _____

Circle the Donor and underline the Magical Agent in the following sentences:

1. The apprentice was poor, and had no sword of his own with which to fight. The sword maker gave him a mighty sword as payment for his years of service.

2. When the little girl got to the store, she realized she didn't have any money to buy a candy bar. But a friend from school was there and shared a candy bar with her.

3. Monkey Medic was able to get a job as a doctor on the ship, thanks to his education from the Monkiversity of Swinging Vines.

4. The car was dirty, but the family was able to wash it clean with the soapy water that was in the bucket.

5. The kids were lost all night until Mario found a trail that led them the way back to camp.

Depending on the story you're telling, there can be all sorts of options for Donors and Magical Agents. Imagine a couple different possible Donors and Magical Agents for these problems.

1. Mina the fire dragon was being attacked by Henry Hosogawa, a Japanic knight. She had to act fast to stop him before he killed her with a sword of ice.

    Donor: Harry, the fire troll, who gives Mina the Magical Agent

    Magical Agent: A blazing club that melts the sword of ice and smashes Henry's hopes

    Donor: Three extra-large and extra-spicy pizzas that give Mina the Magical Agent

    Magical Agent: Fire in her belly, which she uses to burp fire and defeat the knight

2. The audience was getting restless waiting for the guitarist to come onstage to perform.

    Donor: _____

    Magical Agent: _____

    Donor: _____

    Magical Agent: _____

3. The final ten pages of the book would give them nightmares. They shouldn't read them.

    Donor: _____

    Magical Agent: _____

    Donor: _____

    Magical Agent: _____

4. Huck shouldn't travel down the river alone.

    Donor: _____

    Magical Agent: _____

    Donor: _____

    Magical Agent: _____

5. Tom didn't want to paint the fence. He wanted to play now.

    Donor: _____

    Magical Agent: _____

    Donor: _____

    Magical Agent: _____

6. Malfoy didn't want Harry to become a wizard, so he had to stop him from passing the test.

    Donor: _____

    Magical Agent: _____

    Donor: _____

    Magical Agent: _____

7. The mysterious virus could only be killed by eating whole-grain wheat bread, but Mack was allergic to gluten.

    Donor: _____

    Magical Agent: _____

    Donor: _____

    Magical Agent: _____

8. Monty, the thief, wanted to steal the cargo from the truck driver's trailer. He could hardly imagine his luck when Marisol pulled over and went into the café.

Donor: _____

Magical Agent: _____

Donor: _____

Magical Agent: _____

9. Margaux couldn't afford the glasses for sale at Black Eye Glasses and Frame.

Donor: _____

Magical Agent: _____

Donor: _____

Magical Agent: _____

10. The monster in the dark corner didn't want to be seen.

Donor: _____

Magical Agent: _____

Donor: _____

Magical Agent: _____

Bonus questions: See if you can figure out some Donors from stories you know, and beside their name, write a Magical Agent that they donate. I'll do the first one for you.

1. Story: Captain Yogger vs. Kraken Kyle

Donor: First Mate Manfred's volume

Magical Agent: Knowledge of the kraken

2. Story: _____

Donor: _____

Magical Agent: _____

3. Story: _____

Donor: _____

Magical Agent: _____

CHAPTER AVAST AVAST AYE

The two ships are now side-by-side in the ocean, connected by planks and ropes. Captain Yogger is on the Kanadien ship, conversing with their captain, while you and the others watch. The golden-haired Meataloaf lies unconscious on the deck.

You notice the people on this ship appear to be dressed much the same as the Brinitsh ship you encountered awhile ago, but First Mate Manfred insists they are not slavers.

"These are tourists, a long way from home," he assures you.

You nod, feeling very much the same way.

"Thank you, we are forever in your debt," the Kanadien captain bows his head. "You saved the lives of my crew, as well as my ship, and the cargo we've been entrusted to carry. I cannot express my thanks enough."

"Aye. Just be rememberin' t' be careful where ye sail. I might no be around next time t' save yer worm-stained lives," Captain Yogger says. After all this time with him, you still don't know if Yogger is insulting someone when he says things like this or not.

The other captain seems uncertain also as the two of them shake hands.

"Until next time!" the Kanadien captain shouts as Captain Yogger returns to your ship and the two separate.

"Thanks fer th' help, Manny," Captain Yogger says to the first mate as he shakes some of the kraken slime off one of his wooden legs.

"Anytime, Cap." First Mate Manfred closes the volume and the two of them turn to leave. But before they go too far, Captain Yogger stops and glances at you over his shoulder.

"Spat!" he shouts.

You rush over.

"Yes, Captain?"

"Next time ye want t' wake me up," he spits and wipes his mouth with the side of his sleeve, "try knocking."

"Aye, aye, captain," you say, feeling slightly embarrassed.

Captain Yogger winks at you and hobbles back to his cabin.

EXERCISE #22: HELPER AND KING

THE HELPER

The HELPER: a character/thing that contributes to the liquidation of the Act of Villainy.

This character performs the <u>function</u> of helping the other characters defeat the Villain and liquidate the Act of Villainy.

Often they act as supporting characters to the Hero. Sometimes, the Helpers are mini-Heroes who defeat sub-Villains and liquidate mini-AoVs, which helps the Hero perform their function.

An example of this is Monkeyboy. He goes on all the same adventures and helps Monkeyman many times on their quest to defeat the Banana Basher, but at the end of the story, Monkeyman is the Hero because he defeats the Villain and liquidates the AoV.

Identify the Helper by circling them after the following sentences:

1. When my neighbor rescued Monkey Mo Mo from the tree, his wife held the ladder so it wouldn't fall.

Helper: Neighbor / Cat / Tree / Wife / Ladder

2. When the prince came to rescue the princess, his trusty horse carried him safely through the battle.

Helper: Prince / Princess / Horse / Battle

3. The woodsman was able to cut down the tree with ease because his son had sharpened the axe earlier in the day.

Helper: Woodsman / Tree / Son / Axe

4. Monkey Monica clapped and cheered for Captain Yogger as he broke open the coconut.

Helper: Monkey Monica / Captain Yogger / Coconut

5. The dancer drove her car to the concert where she would perform before a large crowd.

Helper: _____

There is no Helper in the following sentences. Read them over, and then create a possible Helper you think could give aid to the Hero.

1. The student drank lots of coffee and worked hard through the night to finish his paper just in time to email it to his teacher.

Possible Helper: _____

2. The dentist came into the room and – after twenty minutes – filled Monkey Monica's nasty cavity.

Possible Helper: _____

3. The child stood outside in the rainstorm to catch the school bus.

        Possible Helper: _____

4. The monkey monarch traditionally is the best dresser, but Monkey Marshall had no sense of fashion.

        Possible Helper: _____

5. During the Monkeyville Riot of 2010, the police were called in to stop the hooligans.

        Possible Helper: _____

List Helpers from stories you know and describe how they help.

Story: _____   Name of Hero: _____

Who helps that Hero? _____   How: _____)_

_____

Story: _____   Name of Hero: _____

Who helps that Hero? _____   How: _____

_____

Story: _____   Name of Hero: _____

Who helps that Hero? _____   How: _____

_____

Story: _____   Name of Hero: _____

Who helps that Hero? _____   How: _____

_____

THE KING

The KING is the sovereign over the thing being fought over (the Princess).

A sovereign is a ruler, a leader, someone with authority and power over something. Usually parents have sovereignty over their children, a teacher has authority over their classroom, and a postal worker has control over the mail. Kings are all around us. We just don't call them Kings.

The King in a story fulfills the function of being the "father" of the Princess. The King can be anything in a story. It can be a character, an object, a belief, a group of people, a culture, an idea, a feeling – and all manner of other things. It is whatever rules – has sovereignty over – something else.

In the follow examples, I will tell you what the Princess is, and you circle the King.

1. The City of Newt Yorker is under attack by the giant Monkzilla.

The Princess is the city. So who is the King?

> The citizens of the city / Monkzilla / The mayor of Newt Yorker / The president

2. All the monkeys fell overboard during a storm.

The monkeys are the Princess. Who is the King?

> The ship / The storm / The sea / The captain

3. The farm dog went for a walk. It found a porcupine and thought it was a new friend. But the porcupine got scared and shot quills into the dog's face.

The dog is the Princess. Who is the King?

> The porcupine / The farm / The farmer / The dog

4. The lightning storm outside was so loud and scary that Monkey Mo Mo was too scared to get out of his bed, even though he was supposed to be in class.

Monkey Mo Mo is the Princess. Who is the King?

> Me (First Mate Manfred) / The storm / The fear / The bed

5. When the family arrived at the water park, they were disappointed to find out that it was closed because summer was over – even though it was such a hot day.

The water park is the Princess. Who is the King?

> The shareholders of the corporation that own the water park /
> The hot weather / The family / The day of the year

Here are some other examples of Kings.

All of us are subject to the laws of physics. Gravity is our King because it has authority over us.

We are Kings over our body, as we have authority over what our body does. If I want to stand up, my body obeys me.

You can be the King over the objects you own. You can take your pencil and use it to write whatever you want.

Also, like Monkey Mo Mo, our feelings can become a kind of King over us, causing us to act in specific ways.

If someone is addicted to something, that addictive substance is like a sovereign King over them.

Kings can also be limited or "temporary." For example, people who work as an employee for a company are under the authority of that company (King), at least when they are working.

I want you to try and find some Kings in stories you know. This will be hard, as Kings are usually very difficult to find. They are usually hidden in some way. Sometimes they are people, but most of the time they are not.

1. Story: *Star Wars*   Character: <u>Luke Skywalker</u>   King: <u>His aunt and uncle</u>

2. Story: *Star Wars*   Character: <u>Obi wan Kenobi</u>   King: <u>The Force</u>

3. Story: *Star Wars*   Character: <u>Han Solo</u>   King: <u>Greed / desire for profit</u>

4. Story: _____ Character: _____ King: _____

5. Story: _____ Character: _____ King: _____

6. Story: _____ Character: _____ King: _____

7. Story: _____ Character: _____ King: _____

8. Story: _____ Character: _____ King: _____

9. Story: _____ Character: _____ King: _____

10. Story: _____ Character: _____ King: _____

If this was a challenge, don't be discouraged. Just come up with your best guess. It may help you to think of what drives, motivates, or controls a character.

SCRATCH YOUR NOGGIN'

List the character functions

1. _____   5. _____

2. _____   6. _____

3. _____   7. _____

4. _____   8. _____

What are the types of Heroes?

1. _____

2. _____   Can there be more than one Helper?

3. _____   _____

Who does the Villain capture?   Who is the King in charge of?

_____   _____

Who tells the Hero about the problem? What is the role of the Donor?

_____   _____

What does a Helper do?   What is a Magical Agent?

_____   _____

Now that you know the functions that characters in a story play, it's time to put a few together and identify them in simple stories.

Here's an example:

There is a car accident, and the driver is badly hurt. A passer-by calls the paramedics, who arrive and revive the person.

Princess: <u>The driver, who is badly hurt and thus needs to be rescued</u>

Dispatcher: <u>The passer-by, who calls the paramedics</u>

Hero: <u>The paramedics, who are able to save the princess</u>

Here's another example:

A sweet old lady's kitten fell down in a deep hole. The lady calls her neighbor, who brings a rope and rescues the kitty.

Act of Villainy: <u>When the kitten fell into a deep hole</u>

Princess: <u>The kitty</u>

King: <u>A sweet old lady (she's the kitten's owner)</u>

Dispatcher: <u>A sweet old lady (she alerts the Hero)</u>

Magical Agent: <u>The rope (the Hero can't rescue the princess without it)</u>

Donor: <u>The neighbor (provides the Hero the Magical Agent)</u>

Hero: <u>The neighbor (because they liquidate the Act of Villainy)</u>

Notice that the old lady and the neighbor each fulfill two functions. The old lady is both the King and Dispatcher. The neighbor is both the Donor and Hero. Characters can fulfill multiple functions within a story.

Now, you work through one.

1. At recess time, Masie pushes Marley off the swing, and he gets hurt. Matthew gets the teacher for help. The teacher comes and helps the hurt child by putting on a band-aid.

Act of Villainy: _____

Villain: _____

Princess: _____

Dispatcher: _____

Magical Agent: _____

Donor: _____

Hero: _____

What type of Hero? _____

2. Matilda's dog jumps up on the table and eats her lunch. Her brother yells and tells their mother. Her mother makes Matilda a new sandwich.

Act of Villainy: _____

Villain: _____

Princess: _____

Dispatcher: _____

Magical Agent: _____

Donor: _____

Hero: _____

What type of Hero? _____

3. Monkeyella's wicked stepmother won't let her go to the ball. Monkeyella's fairy godmother appears and uses her magic wand to do some magic that enables her to go.

Act of Villainy: _____

Villain: _____

Princess: _____

Dispatcher: _____

Magical Agent: _____

Donor: _____

Hero: _____

What type of Hero? _____

4. Horace, a musician, was late for the concert because he was stuck in traffic. But, his best friend, Marcela, was in the car and used her GPS to find a side road they could take to bypass all the traffic. He got to the concert on time and the audience never knew a thing.

Act of Villainy: _____

Villain: _____

Princess: _____

Dispatcher: _____

Magical Agent: _____

Donor: _____

Hero: _____

What type of Hero? _____

5. For some mysterious reason, after the kraken attack, Captain Yogger grew tired of Norman's normal "n" meals. Norman Nopants screamed "Nyet!" when he noticed he was in need of new "n"-named foods. So, the next time they docked in port, Captain Yogger went out and bought him a notebook full of new recipes from the Institute of Nutritious Nutritionists Nurturing Nutrition.

Act of Villainy: _____

Villain: _____

Princess: _____

Dispatcher: _____

Magical Agent: _____

Donor: _____

Hero: _____

What type of Hero? _____

Once you know all the functions and how they interact, you can make a simple story from a list of common words:

Monkey, sword, booty, pirate

The monkey (Hero) rescues the booty (Princess) from the pirate (Villain) by using his sword (Magical Agent).

Now, you try it with these words (you don't have to use them all, but try to use at least four):

Computer hacker, ice cream, money, old man, dancing, radio

_____

_____

_____

Chair, t-Shirt, Monkey Martin, Monkey Mo Mo, honey, crying, water

_____

_____

_____

Cellphone, fan, video game, car, kids, grandparents, coffee cup

_____

_____

_____

Dogs, watermelon, pillow, Medic Mick, important documents, rain

_____

_____

_____

Sharks, map, jelly beans, Captain Yogger, wooden legs, raft

_____

_____

_____

Identify the functions for the characters in the following sentences:

1. No matter how hard the girl tried, she could not comb the tangles out of her hair.

    Function for the girl: _____

    Function for the tangles: _____

2. The man tried his best to fight off the wild bats, but he was helpless to stop as they carried him away to their nest.

      Function for the man: _____

      Function for the bats: _____

3. When the farmer's daughter woke up early and saw the field was on fire, she ran to tell her dad.

      Function for the daughter: _____

      Function for the dad: _____

4. First Mate Manfred drew up the map so Captain Yogger could guide the ship to the island.

      Function for First Mate Manfred: _____

      Function for the map: _____

      Function for Captain Yogger: _____

5. After Monkey Mackenzie told Norman Nopants that Captain Yogger was hungry, Norman went to his cupboard to get some nectarines.

      Act of Villainy: _____

      Function for Monkey Mackenzie: _____

      Function for Norman Nopants: _____

      Function for Captain Yogger: _____

      Function of the cupboard: _____

      Function of the nectarines: _____

      Bonus: Who or what is the Villain? _____

6. During the annual Festival of Trees on Grandpa Ginseng's land, a forest goblin named Gomer Grumble appeared and started to chase the children away. But one child named Penny Pots refused to leave and started to sing the song her grandma taught her instead. When the other kids heard, they all gathered around and joined in singing. Gomer Grumble couldn't stand the music and covered his ears and ran away into the forest, never to return.

      Act of Villainy: _____

      Function of Gomer Grumble: _____

      Function of the festival: _____

      Function of the children: _____

      Function of Penny: _____

      Function of grandma: _____

Function of the song: _____

Function of Grandpa Ginseng: _____

I asked you about seven functions in this story. What is the eighth function that is missing?

_____

Is it actually in the story? Can you find it if it is?

_____

RAISE THE ANCHOR AND SET SAIL

As you were learning about the eight character functions, was there a story that came to your mind that you'd like to write? You can think about a Hero and a Villain if you need something to get you going. What is the Princess the Hero cares about? Is there a Dispatcher that lets the Hero know there is a problem? Don't forget to review the work you did in the exercises to give you ideas.

_____

_____

_____

_____

_____

_____

_____

_____

_____

_____

_____

_____

_____

_____

_____

_____

_____

_____

_____

_____

_____

_____

_____

_____

_____

_____

_____

CHAPTER AVAST AVAST AYE AYE

The sun was hidden behind thick, dark clouds on the day the ship arrived. It was a cool, foggy morning, and one you would never forget.

"I see it! I see the island!" Missy Monkey exclaims as you approach what looks like the island you saw in the golden telescope.

"Oh really?" Monkey Monica crosses her arms and leans against the mast. "Which one is it, then?"

You aren't sure what she means until the ship draws closer and you realize it's just one of what looks to be several hundred islands.

"What is this place?" you ask as a hush falls over the other monkeys. For miles in every direction you see similar-looking islands, many shrouded by a thick layer of fog.

"We be at th' Archipelagos," Captain Yogger states, "a sprawlin' maze o' broken-up islands. Th' one we be wantin' be at th' very end."

As the ship drifts toward the various foggy, green islands, you find your eyes are unable to focus on any specific details of them. Navigating this maze seems impossible!

Monkey Mo Mo is jumping up and down in a terror because of the fog. Mini Mate asks Monkey Monica to take him below deck, and tell him the Garden of Par'o, one of his favorite stories, in the hope it will calm him down.

"Avast! I not seein' it," Mini Mate exclaims as he put the golden telescope back up to his eye. "Thar too many islands. I can no tell which it be!"

"Aye. But it be here," Captain Yogger affirms as he stares down at his map, "we just got t' be findin' it."

You stare out at the many islands and can't help but feel a little discouraged.

"Keep her goin' north an' we be fine," Captain Yogger orders Missy Monkey, who is currently standing at the wheel and working hard to maneuver the ship around the rocky islands.

"How do I know which way north?" she whines as she pulls hard on the wheel to make another turn. "Everything look same here."

"Glad ye asked," Captain Yogger reaches into his pocket and pulls out some kind of hand-held, orange-painted clock.

"What is this for?" you ask as he drops it into your hands.

"If ye be wantin' t' find yer way when yer lost, ye be needin' t' keep yer compass close," Captain Yogger explains.

"A compass?" You stare down at the marks and see how the dial is currently pointing "N." "I've never actually used one of these before."

"Just be keepin' me ship pointed north," Captain Yogger turns your body so you are facing the direction the dial is pointing.

"But there's so many islands in the way."

"That's why it be a maze, Spat." Captain Yogger turns away from you and starts to walk to his cabin. "If ye lose yer way, just get goin' north again. Thar only be one way out o' this mess if ye be wantin' t' get t' th' island."

"But, if the island is on the other end, can't we just go around the Archipelagos?" you call out right before Captain Yogger enters his room.

"Nar, nar! What kind o' story would that be?" he asks with a laugh and shuts the door.

You want to go after him and try to figure out a better plan, but then you catch a glance at Missy Monkey, who looks frustrated to have to be the one on steering duty today.

"You going to help me or what?" she snaps as she pulls on the wheel again to maneuver the ship between two more islands.

"Oh, yeah." You look down at the compass and reposition your body. "Go left around this island . . . and right around the other," you call out instructions.

The islands aren't too close together, but there's something inherently stressful about guiding a large pirate ship around so many jagged rocks.

You wipe some sweat off your brow and hold the compass tightly.

"I sure hope this thing works."

EXERCISE #23: PLOT

So far we have focused on many aspects of plot, but we have not described what plot is. _Plot is a series of events that occur one after another._ Every action we make in life takes place in an order. We do something first, then something else second, another thing third, and so on until we are finished.

Imagine your family has decided they want to go on a big vacation, one where you will fly a long way to another country. Mindstorm a list of everything you can think of that has to happen before you get to your destination. Don't worry about any specific order; just come up with a bunch of ideas. I'll do the first few for you.

1. Pack
2. Get on the plane
3. Drive to the airport
4. Decide where you are going
5. _____
6. _____

7. _____
8. _____
9. _____
10. _____
11. _____
12. _____

All the things you've listed have to happen, but they can't happen in just any order. It would be foolish to get on the plane before you packed, and it would be impossible to get on the airplane before you've decided where you are going.

Take the list you just made (including the options I gave) and place them in order.

1. _____
2. _____
3. _____
4. _____
5. _____
6. _____

7. _____
8. _____
9. _____
10. _____
11. _____
12. _____

The string of events that occur one after another creates a plot.

Take these five actions and put them in the right order.

Taking a shower

1. Go into the bathroom

2. Dry off

3. Turn on the water

4. Realize you're dirty

5. Wash yourself

1. _____

2. _____

3. _____

4. _____

5. _____

Preparing to go to school

1. Eat breakfast

2. Go to school

3. Wake up

4. Get your books

5. Pack a lunch

1. _____

2. _____

3. _____

4. _____

5. _____

Going for a swim

1. Swim

2. Change into bathing suit

3. Get into the water

4. Go to the pool

5. Take a shower

1. _____

2. _____

3. _____

4. _____

5. _____

Taking a test

1. Take the test

2. Sharpen your pencil

3. Sit at a desk

4. Study

5. Go to the testing location

1. _____

2. _____

3. _____

4. _____

5. _____

Make your own list of five steps, in the correct order, for completing some of the following actions:

A. Ordering a hamburger

B. Making a new friend

C. Sword fighting with an evil pirate

D. Baking cookies

E. Having your picture taken

F. Finding buried treasure

G. Teaching a parrot a new trick

Action: _____   Action: _____

1. _____   1. _____
2. _____   2. _____
3. _____   3. _____
4. _____   4. _____
5. _____   5. _____

Action: _____   Action: _____

1. _____   1. _____
2. _____   2. _____
3. _____   3. _____
4. _____   4. _____
5. _____   5. _____

As you can see, things must occur in a certain order if you want to accomplish a task.

Sometimes, it'll be impossible to change the order. Most of the examples above are like this. It's not possible to swim in a pool before you travel and arrive at the pool. But, other times you can change the order of some things, and it does not change the end result. Normally, a person would buy their airplane ticket before they packed for their trip. But it does not have to happen in that order.

You sit down to eat a big dinner – it's a feast – and you are presented with rice, turkey, tomato soup, green beans, hot banana pie, pumpkin ice cream, salad, and potatoes.

What order would you ordinarily eat these items?

First: _____   Fifth: _____
Second: _____   Sixth: _____
Third: _____   Seventh: _____
Fourth: _____   Eighth: _____

But it does not really matter what order you eat them in. (Except to your mother, maybe.)

What is a different order you could eat these items?

First: _____   Fifth: _____
Second: _____   Sixth: _____
Third: _____   Seventh: _____
Fourth: _____   Eighth: _____

Other times, if you do things in a different order, you'll get a different result.

What is the normal order or steps that one would take to make pasta with tomato sauce?

1. _____
2. _____
3. _____
4. _____
5. _____

Now, rearrange these same steps in a way that will produce tomato soup with noodles.

1. _____
2. _____
3. _____
4. _____
5. _____

CHAIN REACTION

You can think of plot like a string of dominos. Once you push one over, there is a chain reaction.

Cross off the things on this list that don't connect to this chain reaction.

Captain Yogger spills coffee on his favorite jacket.

Mini Mate searches the ship for a can of magic potion to get out the stain.

Mini Mate finds it, but it's empty.

We dock our ship at a nearby port town.

Norman Nopants serves nori, nectarines, and noodles for dinner.

In the port town, all the crew search for the magic potion.

Captain Yogger does some exercises.

The monkey mates begin to dance.

Captain Yogger talks to a potion seller.

The potion seller reluctantly sells him some potion.

You (Scurvy Spat) appear in the water.

Captain Yogger pours some of the potion on his stain, and it's removed.

All those things could have happened on the same day and in that order, but some things – like what Norman Nopants served for dinner – are irrelevant to the core plot and are not part of the series of events it took to solve our captain's problem.

Look at the steps involved in the following plot, filling in the details as you go:

Mason, a 15-year-old proboscis monkey who is a pirate's apprentice wants to become a pirate captain himself. How might this cause him to act?

>   First, he pays close attention to what his pirate captain does.
>
>   Second, he trains and builds his _____.
>
>   Third, proves he has the ability to _____.

The plot of the story reflects all the different actions that Mason will take in his quest to achieve his desire.

Take the following characters and their desires, and give them a three-step plot line (think: first, next, last).

1. Mika, a young, curious marmoset, wants to see what happens when she uses a magnifying glass on a banana.

>   First: _____
>
>   Next: _____
>
>   Last: _____

2. Marcos, a short, out-of-shape chimpanzee, lives in the desert, but he wants to be an Olympic bobsled athlete.

>   First: _____
>
>   Next: _____
>
>   Last: _____

3. Mickey, a super-friendly, fast-talking, and hyperactive spider monkey, wants to go to BananaWorld.

>   First: _____
>
>   Next: _____
>
>   Last: _____

4. Moxie, a bold baboon with a pet snake, wants to be popular at school.

>   First: _____
>
>   Next: _____
>
>   Last: _____

5. Miles, a young orphan drill monkey, wants to buy a new bicycle.

      First: _____

      Next: _____

      Last: _____

6. _____ wants _____

      First: _____

      Next: _____

      Last: _____

"HEAVE HO!"

Create a several sentence plot by filling in the following. Name your character, give them 3 characterizations, give them a specific desire, and tell what actions they take to achieve their desire.

Character: _____

Characterizations (3):

1. _____
2. _____
3. _____

Specific desire: _____

Action! (At least 3 steps):

1. _____
2. _____
3. _____
4. _____
5. _____

Character: _____

Characterizations (3):

1. _____
2. _____
3. _____

Specific desire: _____

Action! (At least 3 steps):

1. _____
2. _____
3. _____
4. _____
5. _____

Character: _____

Characterizations (3):

1. _____
2. _____
3. _____

Specific desire: _____

Action! (At least 3 steps):

1. _____
2. _____
3. _____
4. _____
5. _____

Character: _____

Characterizations (3):

1. _____
2. _____
3. _____

Specific desire: _____

Action! (At least 3 steps):

1. _____
2. _____
3. _____
4. _____
5. _____

SCRATCH YER NOGGIN'

1. An Act of Villainy is a _____ that causes one or more _____ to respond and try and solve it.

2. These characters are on the side of _____

3. What or who might cause an Act of Villainy?

_____

_____

_____

_____

4. Manfred hates swimming and getting wet, but is sailing on a boat surrounded by water. This is an example of a _____.

5. What is it that causes characters to make choices? _____

6. What's one way a character could be both fearful and adventurous?

_____.

7. As a story creator, you want to make sure to reveal that your characters have multiple differing and sometimes conflicting _____inside them.

8. Think of two completely different desires a character could have for the following characterization:

Characterization: Everything he/she touches turns to candy

_____   _____

Characterization: Is able to turn invisible whenever he/she wants

_____   _____

9. Sometimes a character has a _____ that makes achieving their desire difficult.

10. Every story begins with a _____. It isn't essential for a story, but it makes it them more gripping.

CHAPTER AVAST AVAST AYE AYE AYE

After several hours of navigating through the foggy waters and past more rocky islands than you've ever seen in your life, you come at last to a gap that leads to the open sea.

"Are we . . . out?" you ask in shock. Part of you thought the Archipelagos would never end.

"We still alive!" Monkey Mo Mo peeks his head up above deck. When he sees all the fog-covered islands are behind them, all the tension goes out of his shoulders.

"Aye. Good work, mateys!" Captain Yogger flashes a grin as he exits his cabin. "An' now, drop anchor. We go fer th' treasure!"

"What? But we didn't find the island," you remind the captain as you glance back at the cluster of islands behind you and then down at the compass. This is definitely the north path, but where the captain is looking, there's no island to be seen.

"It be there, Spat. Right in front o' us," Captain Yogger states.

You aren't sure if he's trying to prank you or not, and so you don't say anything.

"He right!" Monkey Mo Mo shouts as he lowers the golden telescope. "I see it again!"

"Lemme' look!" Mini Mate orders as he takes the telescope in his hands and looks out at the open water.

"Aye," he says confidently, "it thar."

You take the telescope and, sure enough, there's an island right in front of you.

"So . . . it's invisible?" you ask. You aren't sure why you're surprised; very little about this trip has been normal. If there can be talking monkeys, why not invisible islands?

"Last chance, mates." Captain Yogger turns to face the crew. "Any who no be seein' th' island through the telescope be wantin' t' try again before we go?"

You're surprised when the monkeys who haven't been able to see shrug and turn away.

"No point. Not real. Have fun," Monkey Monica replies, and reclines on the deck.

"Fools. Let them stay," Monkey Martin snickers. "More treasure fer us."

"Yo," Monkey M casually leans against the railing. "Treasure sounds cool. But I think I'll stay here. I got enough mystery in my life as it is."

"Aye," Captain Yogger's voice sounds sad.

Monkey Mackenzie looks around nervously, then takes a bold step forward.

"I want to look again," he announces.

"Good, lad. What do ye see?" Captain Yogger asks as Monkey Mackenzie takes the telescope and looks through.

"I . . . I see something," he admits after a second.

"Good. Focus." Captain Yogger puts his hand on his shoulder and gives a reassuring squeeze.

"Yeah . . . I see it!" Monkey Mackenzie jumps up and down. "I see it! I see it!"

Captain Yogger grabs his belly and lets out a loud "yo, ho, ho" which is immediately copied by the higher-voiced Mini Mate.

You can't help but smile as you see the look of joy in Monkey Mackenzie's eyes.

"Great," Monkey Monica scoffs, "now you get him think it real."

Even though she acts like she doesn't care, you suspect part of her is jealous.

"You should try again," you tell her. "It's real. I promise."

"Nah. I no think so," Monkey Monica turns away from you. *"But, if it real, bring back a bean to prove it."*

"Aye, but we be bringin' back more than just one bean," Captain Yogger unsheathes his sword and raises it high in the air. *"Manfred, ye have th' deck!"*

"Aye, aye, Cap," First Mate Manfred replies.

"Ev'ryone else, shove off! Treasure be awaitin'!"

CHAPTER AVAST AVAST AYE ARGH

First Mate Manfred, as well as the other monkeys who couldn't see anything through the telescope, watch with curiosity as Captain Yogger and the rest of you who have seen the island climb into three different rowboats and start rowing to shore.

At least, you trust you're going to shore; you can't see the island with your naked eye, and Captain Yogger has the telescope.

In the boat with you is Mini Mate, Norman Nopants, and Monkey Mo Mo.

In the second, central boat is Captain Yogger, Missy Monkey, and Monkey Mackenzie. The third boat carries your three least favorite monkeys: Monkey Martin, Monkey Morgan, Monkey Morta. You aren't surprised when they all get in the same boat together, though you're relieved they didn't choose to climb into yours.

Part of you is sad First Mate Manfred isn't able to come with, but you understand someone needs to stay behind and guard the ship and watch over all the monkeys who couldn't see the island.

The energy of the group is high and upbeat, but you notice the further your rowboat gets from the main ship, the more tense Monkey Mo Mo gets.

"It dangerous out here. Exposed," Monkey Mo Mo states.

"It's okay," you try to sound reassuring, "we're sailing with Yogger LeFossa, the greatest pirate captain in all the world!"

"Yes. All good. We almost there," Norman affirms.

"How do you know?" The fear in Monkey Mo Mo is clear in his voice. "I can no see anything. I thought we could see it by now. Maybe there no island? Maybe it just a trick, like Monkey Monica say!"

Uh-oh. You didn't expect this. But, you understand where he's coming from. It is a little unnerving to be out, exposed on the water, like this.

"Norman know there is island," the monkey grunts. "Nyet more whine – row!"

The confirmation that the island is there is enough to calm Monkey Mo Mo, and soon, the pirate ship is so far behind you can barely see the flag flapping in the wind.

"Trust. Cap'n Yogger no harm us before. He no start now," Mini Mate declares.

After all you've been through together, you can finally say in all honesty that you agree.

You row hard for a long time – much longer than you expected – and still, there's no sight of the island. You glance over your shoulder and realize you can't really see the ship at all anymore.

"Ya har! We be here!" Captain Yogger hollers back at you from his boat.

His words bring relief to you.

"How can ye tell?" Monkey Martin sneers.

All around you, you see nothing but water. You wish you had the golden telescope with you so you could see land for sure, but Captain Yogger is holding onto it now and is not letting anyone else touch it.

"Be trustin' yer capt'n!" Mini Mate screams. "He say go forward, go forward!"

"Aye," Captain Yogger grins, "full speed ahead, me hearties!"

And just like that, the captain's rowboat is gone. One second they were a few feet away, and the next – vanished!

If you hadn't just have seen it with your own eyes, you might not believe it.

What happened? It's a mystery until you notice the fog.

You glance over at the other rowboat, which is a bit further ahead and thus a bit deeper into the fog. Monkey Martin is smirking.

"LeFossa, LeFossa, da big pirate bossa . . ." Monkey Morgan sings mischievously as he and the others disappear as well.

It's your turn now, the fog is getting thick, but Monkey Mo Mo has stopped rowing with you and is trying to steer the boat around.

"W-w-w-e have to go back," Monkey Mo Mo stammers.

"All is fine. Nyet you whine!" Norman Nopants warns in a gruff voice as he tries to row harder and correct course.

"No . . . No. No! No, no, no!" Monkey Mo Mo is frantic now and is doing everything in his power to turn the boat around.

"Avast! Be calm, broth'r!" Mini Mate hisses.

Thankfully, Monkey Mo Mo is outnumbered, and so the rowboat continues to move into the fog, toward the invisible island – although slowed by Monkey Mo Mo's resistance.

"No! Ahh! NO! I no be slave again!" Monkey Mo Mo grabs his face with both his hands, drops the oar, and stands on the edge of the boat.

"What are you doing?" you try to call to him.

"It trap! LeFossa lie! Come with, brother!" Monkey Mo Mo shouts to Mini Mate.

Mini Mate shakes his head and pulls his hat on tight.

"Nar! He be good human. No trap. Trust."

"I never go into fog again," Monkey Mo Mo says. He can't stop shaking, and a tear trickles down his cheek as he turns his face away.

"I come back to save you. I promise," and with that, Monkey Mo Mo leaps off the boat.

You watch in shock as a small whirlpool opens up and starts to suck Monkey Mo Mo straight into it.

"Wait!" Mini Mate tries to reach for him, but it's no use. Just like you saw happen to Monkey Moby the night you first arrived, Monkey Mo Mo is sucked into a portal and whisked away.

Mini Mate turns the rowboat around, but the whirlpool closes as quickly as it formed, and soon everything is calm again on the sea. Aside from his oar, floating on top of the water, there's no sign Monkey Mo Mo was ever with you.

"Shiver me timbers . . ." Mini Mate curses under his breath.

The silence is hard to bear as the three of you sit quietly in the boat.

"Is . . ." you struggle to find the words to say, "is he going . . . I mean, do you know where he went?"

Mini Mate doesn't say anything, but his fingers are wrapped so tightly around the edge of the boat that his knuckles are turning white.

"Norman say go forward," Norman Nopants grumbles after a moment.

"Aye," Mini Mate agrees, "nothing t' be done now. Time t' go."

You can't help but feel sad as you grab your oar and, somewhat grimly, row straight into the mist and the unknown.

EXERCISE #24: GAPS AND EXPECTATION

Things don't always go the way we expect them to.

If a character wanted something, took action to get it, and then got it right away without any problems, it wouldn't make for a very interesting story. We like stories that have twists and turns, where things don't work out the way we – or the characters – expect them to.

When a character expects things will go one way and then discovers they're going another, we call it a gap. It is what you'd imagine: a gap between someone's expectations and reality.

When you first heard us monkey mates speak, you were shocked, right? That's because where you come from, monkeys don't talk. Listening to monkeys have conversations created a gap for you.

Go through the following sentences and answer whether there is a gap or not.

1. Michael went to the store to buy some banana bread, but found they were all sold out!

   Gap or no gap? _____

2. Magda was crushed when she brought her antique necklace to the pawn shop – thinking it would be worth a lot – but they only offered her five banana bucks.

   Gap or no gap? _____

3. Macie had been preparing for the concert for months, and when she went up on stage that night, she sang beautifully.

   Gap or no gap? _____

4. The weather baboon predicted a big storm that night, so mom brought all her flowers inside to keep them safe from hail. Sure enough, that night was one of the worst storms of the year.

   Gap or no gap? _____

5. Marvin the Mandrill went to the hair salon expecting to get his mohawk trimmed. After the stylist was done, he looked in the mirror and was shocked to see his beautiful hair buzzed short.

   Gap or no gap? _____

Two of those sentences did not contain gaps. Rewrite them so that they contain a gap.

1. _____

   _____

2. _____

   _____

Imagine you are on your way to the bus stop to get to school. But instead of finding the bus, you see Malachi, the school bully. That wasn't what you expected! He lives on the other side of the forest. What is he doing here?

Finding Malachi was one gap. What might be some other gaps that could have occurred? Instead of finding the school bus, you find. . .

1. _____
2. _____
3. _____

RESPONSE

Because I described Malachi as a bully, you probably had some expectations for him. But, what if instead of beating you up, he gave you a high-five and complimented your outfit. Whoa! That would be a really unexpected response, and thus another gap.

Write down six possible things Malachi could do that you wouldn't expect from a bully.

1. _____   4. _____
2. _____   5. _____
3. _____   6. _____

Imagine you see a friend and you say, "Hey, good morning." You'd probably expect them to say "hi" back. What are some other things they could say or do that you would not expect, and thus create a gap?

1. _____   4. _____
2. _____   5. _____
3. _____   6. _____

GAPS IN SENSE

Have you ever tasted something that you expected to be salty and found it was actually sweet? It can be really confusing when your senses are tricked.

Imagine you saw a cute cat, but when you went to pet it, you realized it was actually a skunk!

1. You found a beautiful flower and went to smell it, but instead of smelling nice, it smelled like:

_____! Or _____! Or _____!

2. You thought you were taking a bite of a piece of chocolate, but in reality, it was

_____! Or _____! Or _____!

276

3. After a long day, you went to go lie in your comfortable bed, but you had no idea it was filled with:

_____! Or _____! Or _____!

4. You thought you heard someone calling your name, but. . .

_____!

Or _____!

5. A soft, fluffy bird landed on your shoulder, but. . .

_____!

Or _____!

6. You thought you saw a gold doubloon at the bottom of the pool, but. . .

_____!

Or _____!

GAPS IN LOCATION

Have you ever gotten lost? That's a gap in your location. You thought you were going one place, but turned out to be somewhere else. Maybe you thought your hotel would be in a different location. Or, you expected the beach to only be a five-minute walk, instead of thirty minutes.

Use your imagination to come up with some gaps in location for the following characters:

1. When Malloy McFarland found a room at a discount hotel, he promised his wife Moya it would be just as close to the tourist sites as a regular-priced hotel.
<u>When they arrived they discovered the discount hotel was a thirty-minute bus ride to the center of the city.</u>

2. The city bus looked different than normal, but Martyn and Maisy didn't think anything about it as they got on. They were excited to be going to Banana Republic to buy some new clothes.

_____

_____

3. When Chario read the brochure for summer camp, it looked like it would be a week of fun in the jungle with other white-headed capuchins.

_____

_____

4. When Malcolm the Space Monkey landed his spaceship on the newly discovered Planet Banananern, he expected to find it devoid of life like the satellite photographs showed.

_____

_____

5. Sammy the Slug always wanted to go to SlimeLand, and so he saved up all his money to go.

_____

_____

GAPS IN ROUTINE / TRADITION

One way to really confuse a character is to present them with a gap in their routine or tradition.

List some routines and traditions you have.

1. Every Sunday at 2:00 p.m. you play coconut football with the golden tamarins in your neighborhood.

2. _____

3. _____

4. _____

5. _____

Now, create a gap for each one.

1. You arrive at 2:00 p.m., but find a gang of orangutans have taken over the field.

2. _____

3. _____

4. _____

5. _____

GAPS GALORE

Gaps can occur in everything. Life is full of gaps. Try to think of a few from your life where something did not go like you expected.

1. _____

_____

2. _____

_____

3. _____

_____

Can you think of any specific gaps you, Scurvy Spat, have seen since coming aboard the ship? Tell me about them here.

1. _____

_____

2. _____

_____

3. _____

_____

"HEAVE HO!"

Think of one of your favorite stories: _____

1. What is one major gap you can remember for the <u>Hero</u>?

_____

_____

2. What is one major gap you can remember for the <u>Villain</u>?

_____

_____

3. If the <u>Princess</u> was a character, what is one major gap you can remember for them?

_____

_____

4. If the <u>Donor</u> was a character, what is one major gap you can remember for them?

_____

_____

One gap can create another.

1. It's Maxwell's birthday, and he expects his mom to let him go play with his best friend. But, when he asks, his mom says "no." That creates a gap for him.

2. Maxwell's mom expects Maxwell to handle that well, but he doesn't. He throws a tantrum and whines and complains. This creates a gap for her.

3. Maxwell expects his tantrum will work to get his mom to change her mind, but it doesn't. His mother still refuses and sends him to his room. This creates a gap for him.

4. Maxwell goes and pouts in his room believing his mom is trying to ruin his life. But, when his parents call Maxwell to come out of his room for dinner, he discovers all of his friends are there for a surprise party. His mom had planned this the whole time! This creates a gap for him. (Sometimes gaps can be positive.)

Create your own chain of gaps, where one gap leads to another.

1. _____

_____

2. _____

_____

3. _____

_____

4. _____

_____

Do it again for a different chain of gaps.

1. _____

_____

2. _____

_____

3. _____

_____

4. _____

_____

CHAPTER AVAST AVAST ARGH

One second, you see nothing but open ocean, the next, nothing but fog. Inside, the very air itself ripples and fluctuates. You are in the dark, blind, for only a moment, before light sweeps the darkness away like a flood. You see you're floating in the bay of a beautiful, tropical island. Your heart skips a beat at the sight of it.

In all your life, you've never seen water so blue, sand so white, or rocks with such a dynamic mix of red and black. This island looks like something straight out of a fairytale, complete with giant, tropical trees and wild, exotic birds soaring above. You are grateful magic has hidden this island, because – at least in your world – you're sure people would have long ago plundered this place in order to transform it into an expensive resort.

"We made it!" you exclaim and feel a wave of relief. Captain Yogger wasn't tricking you. Although that is good news, it means Monkey Mo Mo got scared for nothing, and that fact breaks your heart.

You see Captain Yogger, Missy Monkey, and Monkey Mackenzie on the shore, and start to row toward them, when all of a sudden, it dawns on you that you don't see the others.

"Wait a second. . . "

Monkey Martin, Monkey Morgan, and Monkey Morta, and the other two rowboats are all missing!

"Blasted blimey banana-lovin' mutinous monkeys!" Mini Mate says and then begins to screech a stream of wild monkey sounds that you would not be surprised to be curses.

"What happened?" you ask Captain Yogger as your rowboat reaches shore.

"They stole the map!" Monkey Mackenzie shouts. "They stole our boat and the map!"

You follow Missy Monkey's stare and spot the two boats traveling around the Island.

"Nyet. Fools. You want for Norman to chase them?" Norman Nopants asks as he cracks his knuckles.

"Nar, nar." The pain in Captain Yogger's voice is thick. "Let them go. Thay made thar choice."

You thought Captain Yogger looked sad when so many monkeys chose to stay on the boat, but it's clear from his face this hit him even harder.

". . .Monkey Mo Mo?" Monkey Mackenzie asks.

"Gone," Mini Mate admits grimly.

Captain Yogger turns his eyes away from everyone.

"I were afraid o' that."

Even though you've finally made it to the island, you can't help but feel sad over the loss of Monkey Mo Mo and now the map. After working so hard to get here, it doesn't feel fair.

You sit down in the sand and start sifting sand in your hands, feeling the individual grains run through your fingers. Did you really come all this way just to fail?

You look up at the remainder of your team and see they all appear very frazzled. Mini Mate, for one, can't stop pacing around and mumbling curses under his breath, while Norman Nopants looks like he's ready to fight. But, as far as you can tell, the only fight left is the one to hold back tears.

"No fair," Monkey Mackenzie whines.

"No," you agree, "not fair at all."

You turn around and stare into the wild jungle that covers the island.

"You want us to go in there . . . without the map?" you repeat Captain Yogger's words.

"Aye. Thay got our map, but we still be havin' our memory," Captain Yogger states confidently. "We can get t' th' treasure. Ye all been studyin' with me first mate. Do ye remember th' way?"

You scratch your head. You spent most of the time studying story, not the map. Does he really think it's possible to find the way through that thick jungle and to the treasure?

"I 'member some," Missy Monkey states.

"Me too," agrees Monkey Mackenzie.

They turn to look at you and ask, "What do you remember?"

You aren't sure what to say. You saw the map a few times, but Captain Yogger never really gave you a clear look at it.

"I . . . I don't know. Some, maybe," you reply weakly.

"We nyet get far on pieces," Norman Nopants grunts.

"What do we do then?" Missy Mate crosses her arms. "We can no just sit here all day."

"She right," Mini Mate finally says something. For the last ten minutes, he's been silently staring out at the water where Monkey Mo Mo was last seen. But now, he moves away from the water and heads toward the rest of you. "We find th' way."

"How?" you ask. "We don't have the map."

Mini Mate grumbles something under his breath, pushes past you, and heads straight for the jungle.

You stare at him as he stops at the foot of the trees.

"Ye comin'?" he asks. "Thar be no time t' waste."

Missy Monkey nods and starts to follow after him. You exchange a look with Norman Nopants and shrug.

"May as well try," you say.

And so, without another word, you, Captain Yogger, and the other monkeys head into the jungle.

EXERCISE #25: BEGINNING, MIDDLE, END

In the lesson on plot, you were taught that a plot is a series of events that happen one after another. Similarly, every story has a beginning, middle and end. Sometimes these are called act one, act two and act three. This is because most events in life have a beginning, middle and end. _Thinking in terms of beginning, middle and end can help you organize all of the events that happen in a story._

I am going to make a list of the steps that take place in order to eat a meal. I will put them in the right order, like I had you do in the lesson on plot.

Eating a meal:

1. Deciding what the meal will be
2. Gathering the items for the meal
3. Chopping, slicing, mixing, cooking
4. Setting the table
5. Serving the meal
6. Eating
7. Clearing the table
8. Washing the dishes
9. Putting everything away
10. Cleaning the kitchen

Beginning, middle and end is a way to summarize all of the steps in a plot.

> Beginning: Prepare and serve the meal (items 1-5)
>
> Middle: Eat the meal (item 6)
>
> End: Clean up and put things away after the meal (items 7-10)

To find the beginning, I needed to look at the list and determine all of the things that have to happen before the main thing can occur. Before you can eat a meal, you have to decide what to eat, prepare it, and serve it (items 1-5).

Next, I looked for the end. I examined all the things that needed to happen before the event is completely finished. This will be the end. After you eat a meal, the job isn't done until everything is cleaned up (items 7-10).

This then left me with the middle, all the things that happen in between (item 6).

Now it's your turn.

Make a list of all of the things that must happen for a caterpillar to become a butterfly. Put them in the right order. (Write down as many steps that you think are necessary. You do not have to use all of the lines if you don't need them. You can also add lines if you need more.)

1. _____
2. _____
3. _____
4. _____
5. _____
6. _____
7. _____
8. _____

Now summarize all of the steps by finding their beginning, middle, and end.

Beginning: _____ Item(s): _____

Middle: _____ Item(s): _____

End: _____ Item(s): _____

2. Make a list of the things that must happen in order for you to buy new clothes. Put them in the correct order.

1. _____   5. _____

2. _____   6. _____

3. _____   7. _____

4. _____   8. _____

Now summarize all of the steps by finding their beginning, middle, and end.

Beginning: _____ Item(s): _____

Middle: _____ Item(s): _____

End: _____ Item(s): _____

3. Make a list of the things that must happen in order for you to travel from one place to another. (It can be going from home to school, going from school to the store, going from home to a friend's house, going on vacation from your home to the lovely Endoniceian Port Pitogo, or wherever you want.)

      Where are you starting from? _____

      Where are you going? _____

1. _____   5. _____

2. _____   6. _____

3. _____   7. _____

4. _____   8. _____

Now summarize all of the steps by finding their beginning, middle, and end.

Beginning: _____ Item(s): _____

Middle: _____ Item(s): _____

End: _____ Item(s): _____

4. Make a list of the things that happen during a storm. (It can be a snowstorm, thunderstorm, hailstorm, rainstorm, windstorm, tornado, or any other kind of storm you can imagine.)

What is storming around you? _____

1. _____   5. _____
2. _____   6. _____
3. _____   7. _____
4. _____   8. _____

Now summarize all of the steps by finding their beginning, middle, and end.

Beginning: _____ Item(s): _____

Middle: _____ Item(s): _____

End: _____ Item(s): _____

Mindstorm a list of activities/actions. It can include things you do every day, things you rarely do, something you did in the past, or something you want to do in the future. They can be big things, small things, something important or something insignificant.

1.   Becoming a pirate   9. _____
2.   Swabbing the deck   10. _____
3.   Smelling a stinky monkey   11. _____
4.   _____   12. _____
5.   _____   13. _____
6.   _____   14. _____
7.   _____   15. _____
8.   _____   16. _____

Select items from your list and find their beginning, middle, and end.

1. _____   2. _____

Beginning: _____   Beginning: _____

Middle: _____   Middle: _____

End: _____   End: _____

3. _____   5. _____

    Beginning: _____   Beginning: _____

    Middle: _____   Middle: _____

    End: _____   End: _____

4. _____   6. _____

    Beginning: _____   Beginning: _____

    Middle: _____   Middle: _____

    End: _____   End: _____

PLOT PROGRESSION

A way to see the beginning, middle, and end of a story is to examine how the series of events (the plot) must progress before there can be a conclusion. The beginning consists of the events that must happen before the middle can even occur. The middle contains of all of the events that happen as the story progresses towards an ending. The end consists of all the events that must happen to bring the story to an actual close.

For example, in *Star Wars* the beginning consists of: Darth Vader taking Princess Leia captive, Luke finding the hidden message in R2D2, Luke finding Obi Wan Kenobi, and the massacre of Luke's family. The middle consists of: finding a ship that will transport them to the Rebels, being captured by the Death Star, freeing Princess Leia, Obi Wan Kenobi fighting Darth Vader, and Luke and the others escaping. The end consists of: the battle to blow up the Death Star.

1. Think of a story you like: _____

Describe what happens in the beginning:

_____

_____

Describe what happens in the middle:

_____

_____

_____

_____

Describe what happens at the end:

_____

_____

2. Think of another story you like: _____

Describe what happens in the beginning:

_____

_____

Describe what happens in the middle:

_____

_____

_____

_____

Describe what happens at the end:

_____

_____

3. Think of a third story you like: _____

Describe what happens in the beginning:

_____

_____

Describe what happens in the middle:

_____

_____

_____

_____

Describe what happens at the end:

_____

_____

PERSPECTIVE

In the following sentences, see if you can identify what stage of the story these characters are in.

Circle your choice:

1. After a long day of canoeing across Banana Bay, Monkey Mocha finally arrived back home.

Beginning / Middle / End

2. After leaving Port Plantain, we encountered a furious storm. Instead of having faith in Captain Yogger, Monkey Mo Mo was sure the ship was about to break apart and we'd all be doomed.

Beginning / Middle / End

3. The baby pollywog Kimberly broke out of the egg and looked around the sea for the first time.

Beginning / Middle / End

4. Mary spotted our ship in Port Popoulu. She was a shy and nervous monkey, and watched the crew from a distance.

Beginning / Middle / End

5. After a long and tedious journey, the wild tiger was finally getting accustomed to her new home at the zoo, when all of a sudden, an earthquake shook the city and flung the gates open.

Beginning / Middle / End

Some of these were probably easier than others. For example, in example 3, you likely assumed this was the beginning. However, it could also be the end if the story was about the baby pollywog being born, or it could be the middle if it's a story about Kimberly's mother.

It's not possible to define the beginning, middle, and end of something until that something has actually ended. When you are in the middle of a story, you often don't know what stage you're in. Are you just about to end something or are you still just at the beginning?

Let's say you are a slave to Captain Orangebeard. You are told you have to work for an entire year before you are set free. When that year is almost over, you think you are near the end of your terrible story. But, Captain Orangebeard is evil, so when the year is over, you are told you must work for another year before you are set free.

This kind of unexpected delay happens all the time in life.

Imagine you're a headhunter taking a Sunday stroll through the forest. You've traveled this trail many times before, and you know you're almost at the end of it, but then something unexpected happens that causes a delay. Mindstorm a few possibilities.

1. _____

2. _____

3. _____

The opposite can also occur. Let's say you have only been a slave to a Captain Orangebeard for three months. You have nine months left (you think). But, then the Brintish Navy captures Captain Orangebeard's ship, takes him prisoner, and sets you free. The end of your story happened much sooner than you expected.

Have you ever been in a story that ended sooner than you expected? Tell me about it in a few sentences.

_____

_____

_____

Likewise, when an author is creating a story it is often difficult for them to see the beginning, middle, and end until they've worked out the entire story. This is why I have placed this lesson at the end of our story. You're getting close to finding the Grove of Eternal Beans. You are almost to the end. Or are you?

SHAPE

You may be wondering what the purpose is for finding the beginning, middle, and end, especially if someone cannot know what the beginning, middle, and end is until after the story is over. There are many reasons, but as this is an introductory class, I will only share two. The first is shape.

Shape? What do I mean by shape? Well, different stories have different shapes, just like different things have different shapes.

Describe the shape of the following things. (If you can't describe one in words, you can draw a picture in the margin.)

An apple: Round

A banana: _____

A palm tree: _____

An oak tree: _____

An island: _____

A jelly bean: _____

An airplane: _____

A sword: _____

A snowmonkey: _____

Here are trickier ones. (Don't hurt your mind trying to answer all of these.)

A cloud: _____

A shooting star: _____

Water: _____

A memory: _____

Happiness: _____

Anger: _____

Your favorite book: _____

Fireworks: _____

A roller coaster: _____

Most things have shapes and the challenge is finding a way to describe that shape. The way we describe the shape of a story is by identifying the beginning, middle, and end. A common shape of a story is to have a medium-sized beginning, a long middle, and a short-to-medium-sized end. But, stories can take all kinds of shapes.

Remember the example of making a meal. The beginning consists of deciding what to make, gathering the ingredients, and cooking. The middle is eating the meal. The end is cleaning up the meal. An order something like this will be true for all meals, but not all meals have the same shape.

What if you decided to make a simple meal, with ingredients you already had, and that cooked quickly? The beginning may only take you 20 minutes.

Then, let's say you are a slow eater, and it takes you 60 minutes to eat this meal. Thus, the length of the middle would be three times larger than the beginning.

Last, you hate doing dishes, so you eat on paper plates, and the end – putting everything away and cleaning up – only takes five minutes.

Twenty minutes, sixty minutes and five minutes. This is the shape of one "story" for making the meal.

1. Describe what could cause the shape of a meal to have a very long beginning, a medium-length middle, and a medium-length end.
Long beginning:

_____

_____

How many minutes: _____
Medium middle:

_____

_____

How many minutes: _____
Medium end:

_____

_____

How many minutes: _____

2. Describe what could cause the shape of a meal to have a very short beginning, a medium-length middle, and a very long end.
Very short beginning:

_____

_____

How many minutes: _____

Medium middle:

_____

_____

How many minutes: _____
Very long end:

_____

_____

How many minutes: _____

3. Describe what could cause the shape of a meal to have a medium beginning, a very short-length middle, and a very short end.
Medium beginning:

_____

_____

How many minutes: _____
Very short middle:

_____

_____

How many minutes: _____
Very short end:

_____

_____

How many minutes: _____

Can you see how the shape of a meal will create a different experience for the people involved in that meal? A rushed and hectic meal is a different thing than a two-hour leisurely lunch.

Because different shapes of the same thing create different experiences, an author needs to be aware of the shape of the story they are telling.

BUILDING BLOCKS

A second reason to find the beginning, middle, and end of your story is that it is a valuable tool writers use to help them build big, long, or complicated stories.

You don't need to think about it if you are writing a short, simple story like this:

"Mini Mate wanted to be more like Captain Yogger, so he attached wooden planks to his legs. Now, wherever he goes, Mini Mate hobbles too."

But, what if you are writing a thousand page novel, or a television series that will run for years? This is like building a tall skyscraper. Big buildings need to be carefully planned out with a lot of engineering work, so they do not fall down. Likewise, big stories need a lot of engineering work in the form of working out beginnings, middles, and ends.

The longest, most complicated story all people experience is the story of their own life. Just like everything else, a person's life has a beginning, middle, and end.

Beginning: Birth and childhood

Middle: Adulthood

End: Decline and death

As this is a big story, you can take any part of this and break it into smaller pieces. For example, you can take the end: "Decline and Death," and find the beginning, middle, and end to just this part.

Beginning: Retirement

Middle: Declining health

End: Final sickness and death

Sad, huh? But, you can do the same thing for the beginning of your story, "Birth and Childhood."

Describe a beginning, middle, and end for "Birth and Childhood."

Beginning: _____

Middle: _____

End: _____

Now do it for the middle, "Adulthood"

Beginning: _____

Middle: _____

End: _____

You can break the story down even further. Take the Middle you wrote above for "Adulthood" and describe a beginning, middle, and end for it.

Beginning: _____

Middle: _____

End: _____

By breaking down your story in this way, you can create a strong skeleton or scaffolding for your story that will enable you to build it up like a tall and strong skyscraper.

"HEAVE HO!"

THE BEGINNING

The beginning consists of the events that must happen before the middle can even occur. Often, these are things that are overlooked. But, the things that happen in the beginning set up everything that follows in the story. In fact, some people call the beginning the "set up."

For example, we may not realize that in order to make a meal an essential step is to choose what you are going to eat. But, the menu sets up everything that happens later.

Story #1. Think of a story you know well: _____

What are some things that happen in the beginning of this story that must happen before the middle can occur?

_____

What does it set up in the rest of the story?

_____

_____

Story #2. Think of another story: _____

What are some things that happen in the beginning of this story that must happen before the middle can occur?

_____

What does it set up in the rest of the story?

_____

_____

THE END

The end consists of all the events that must happen to bring the story to a final and complete close. Some people call it the "resolution" because it is where the problems – the Acts of Villainy – of the story are resolved.

As it's usually best to find the beginning and end of a story before looking for the middle, I've placed the end here, out of order, so you can do middle last. (Isn't that confusing?)

Story #1 from above: _____

What are some things that must happen at the end before the story can come to a final and complete close?

_____

_____

What things are resolved at the end?

_____

_____

Story #2 from above: _____

What are some things that must happen at the end before the story can come to a final and complete close?

_____

_____

What things are resolved at the end?

_____

_____

THE MIDDLE

The middle contains of all of the events that the characters engage in that move the story towards an ending. The middle is where the step-by-step progression towards an ending occurs.

Story #1 from above: _____

What are some things that happen in the middle of this story that move it toward an end?

_____

_____

_____

_____

Story #2 from above: _____

What are some things that happen in the middle of this story that move it toward an end?

_____

_____

_____

_____

CHAPTER AVAST AVAST ARGH AYE

You do your best to push branches and vines out of the way, but it's so thick in this jungle you can hardly see anything.

Whatever trees live in here, they're completely unlike anything you ever read about in school. The leaves here are all sorts of colors: fall colors, like orange, red, and yellow, but also strange ones, like blue and purple. And on every tree hang oranges, apples, and grapes that are larger than bowling balls. You're tempted to stop and pick some, but there's no time; you're on a mission.

Mini Mate has done a great job of leading the journey through the jungle, but even with his help, you've still gotten lost and circled the same crystal blue pond at least four times.

But, you expected this to happen; what you didn't expect was for Captain Yogger to remain silent the whole time. Instead of leading like he has the entire time you've known him, he now appears to be perfectly content to hang behind the group and watch as you all wade through mud, scramble over prickly bushes, and climb around rocky cliffs in an attempt to find your way.

"Why isn't Captain Yogger helping?" you ask Monkey Mackenzie as you each take turns leaping over a section of sandy sinkholes.

"What you mean? He here."

"But he's not leading. He's read the map more than any of us. He should know the way," you insist.

Monkey Mackenzie shrugs.

"I no question Captain Yogger. He no always make sense, but he good leader and know what he doing."

You know that Monkey Mackenzie is right, but you still feel a bit confused by it.

"Hey!" Mini Mate shouts. "I think I found it!"

Excitement leaps up in your chest.

"You did?" you exclaim as you leap over the last sinkhole, push past some vines, and step out into a clearing on a hill. Running down and across the hillside are row after row of greenish-purple bushes.

"Aye. Well-done, Mini Mate!" Captain Yogger affirms as he steps out of the bush and into the clearing. "This be it."

After such a long journey, you're overcome with relief at finally arriving at the fabled Grove of Eternal Beans.

But, as you get close to the bushes, you don't see any signs of jelly beans. Aside from being a strange color, the bushes seem pretty ordinary.

"Is this really it?" you ask, unable to hide the disappointment in your voice. You expected the Grove of Eternal Beans to actually have some jelly beans.

"Avast! Look!" Mini Mate reaches in and pulls out an empty branch.

You move closer to the bushes and realize that there does seem to have been something growing here.

"What it mean?" Missy Monkey scratches her head.

"It mean we too late!" Mini Mate exclaims. "Ev'ry bean been plucked!"

You can hardly believe it, but it does seem every bush on the hill has been picked clean.

Another wave of disappointment hits you. It seems like nothing is turning out as you expected when you first set out on this quest.

"There!" Norman shouts. He's climbed a high hill and points toward the ocean.

When you climb up the hill – sure enough – you see the three mutinous monkeys, Martin, Morgan, and Morta, by the water, dragging a large sack full of something into one of the two stolen rowboats. Jelly beans!

"They won?" Missy Monkey's voice quivers as she speaks.

"It look so," Monkey Mackenzie sighs.

"Avast," Captain Yogger strokes his chin. "It look like we're not yet at th' end o' our story."

"Norman will end it," Norman Nopants cracks his knuckles. "Norman get beans back."

He looks like he's about to run down the hill after the mutinous monkeys, but Captain Yogger sticks his arm out and stops him.

"Nar. Let them go."

"But . . . they stole the treasure!" you exclaim. "It isn't fair!" After everything you've been through to get here, you can't imagine just giving up now.

"Thay stole a treasure, but not th' treasure. Those beans be doin' nothing fer monkeys but addin' another foul smell t' them, like the one they got after they stole one o' me beans," Captain Yogger winks at you and starts to wander away. "Follow along, me hearties! We just finished the middle o' our story, an' we got a bit further t' go before we hit th' end."

You desperately want to go with Norman after those thieving, mutinous monkeys and rescue the jelly beans, but for some reason, Captain Yogger doesn't seem the least concerned about it.

"Like I say," Monkey Mackenzie pats you on the back, "Captain Yogger know what he doing."

"I hope so," you say with a frown as you and the remaining few monkeys go with him deeper into the jungle.

CHAPTER AVAST AVAST ARGH AYE AYE

You follow Captain Yogger through more jungle, which is less dense than before. You are confused when he leads you to a cliff wall. Captain Yogger says nothing, but begins to clear away some of the leaves and bushes with his sword.

"What's he doing?" you ask Mini Mate. He doesn't answer; the smaller monkey looks as confused as you feel.

It doesn't take long before Captain Yogger pulls away enough brush for you to see there's a secret cave entrance hidden in the rocks.

"Whoa!" Missy Monkey's eyes grow wide.

"Come on in," Captain Yogger says as he disappears into the cave.

You feel afraid – only because it's a dark cave – but after everything you've been through, you have no reason to doubt Captain Yogger. You and the other monkeys take cautious steps into the darkness.

It takes your eyes a few seconds to adjust to the change in light, but soon you are able to see a glow coming from deep within.

You put your hand against the rocks and take one careful step after another through the cave until you come around a corner and find a massive underground cavern filled with glowing, crystal blue water. The light reflects against the cavern walls and creates a beautiful shimmer. Hanging high above the water on the cavern ceiling are long, tooth-like slices of rock that look like icicles.

You find yourself so distracted by the dancing patterns the reflected water makes against the walls and the strange rock formations that you don't notice the giant trees growing by the water until Monkey Mackenzie points them out.

"Bananas!" he squeals.

You lower your eyes and next to the pool you see several large oak trees that have bright bunches of yellow bananas hanging from their branches. You've never seen a banana tree in person before, but you're pretty sure they don't look anything like oaks.

The monkeys whisper amongst each other and scratch their heads in confusion.

"This a test?" Missy Monkey asks apprehensively. You understand her concern; those bananas look ripe and ready to eat.

"No," Captain Yogger grins, "this be yer treasure."

The monkeys stare at him and blink several times, but make no movement toward the bananas. "Come on. Eat!" Captain Yogger lets out a hearty laugh, reaches up for one and plucks it off the tree. He then hands it to Mini Mate.

Mini Mate darts his head back and forth between the glowing banana and Captain Yogger.

"Eat?" he asks after a short pause. "Ye say no eat bananas."

"Yar, these be no ordinary bananas. This be yer treasure, so eat. No–" Captain Yogger pauses for dramatic effect – "Feast!"

Mini Mate hesitates, then reluctantly peels the banana and takes a nibble. As soon as he does, his eyes grow wide.

"It be delicious!" he exclaims, and suddenly the whole thing is in his mouth.

The other monkeys start to jump up and down and, before long, they're all swinging from branch to branch collecting bananas, eating them, and leaping into the cave pool. Even Norman Nopants has joined them and is smiling for the first time since you've met him.

"What happen to 'Norman only eat things that start with 'N'?'" Missy Monkey asks him as he pops another banana into his mouth.

"It no problem. Banana start with 'b', but inside has two 'n.' Norman only eat inside of banana," he explains with a laugh.

"Huh?" the monkeys all stop eating and stare at him.

You're the only one who laughs at the joke and think this may be the beginning of Norman opening up to other kinds of food.

The other monkeys scratch their heads, but after a few seconds they give up trying to understand and resume eating.

"So . . . I'm confused," you say to Captain Yogger as the monkeys gorge themselves. "I thought you didn't want them to eat bananas? I thought it made them stink?"

"Aye, Scurvy Spat. But, here be no ordinary banana. Thay be acquirin' no stink from eatin' these. An' thay also have th' power t' do a lil' bit o' healing. In time, yer goin' t' smell a lot less cursed smell from these monkey mates."

Now you are the one scratching your head.

"Healing? You mean they won't smell anymore?" If that's true, it's going to make living on a ship with monkeys a lot easier.

"These bananas not be curin' all o' their stink. But, lil' by lil' thay be gettin' better. Eventually, some day, thay be free t' be eatin' normal bananas again. But, thay still be stinky fer other reasons – thay still bein' monkeys, after all!"

"Really? That's incredible."

"It bein' a worthy treasure, aye?"

All of a sudden, it hits you. This is the real treasure; this is what the monkeys have been needing. Their smell was a problem Captain Yogger cared about. He considered it an Act of Villainy, so he took action and, using the magical agent of these bananas, he liquidated it for them.

You look at the monkeys laughing and playing without a care in the world.

"You did this for them," you say, understanding what function he played in this story.

"Aye."

You look at him with new admiration. But, then you realize something else. What about Monkey Mo Mo? He's gone and still stinks. You also grieve for all the other monkeys who aren't here. What about the monkeys who chose to go their own way? And what about all the monkeys still on the ship? Their Act of Villainy hasn't been resolved.

You turn to the Captain. "Why didn't you tell the other monkeys about this sooner? Like Monkey Mo Mo or Monkey Moby? Or even Monkey Maxine? They'd never have left if they knew about this."

"If thay knew th' quest be fer them, thay'd be stayin' fer the wrong reasons," Captain Yogger explains, "I needed t' know who be truly wantin' t' find treasure fer others. I be seekin' Seeker Heroes."

"I'm sorry, I still don't understand."

"Remember them monkeys who stole me bean? Ye understand why thay stink so bad after thay ate it?"

You don't, so Captain Yogger explains, "It be a magical jelly bean from this very island."

"So . . . this whole quest was never for you and your breath? You didn't need the magic jelly beans after all?"

"Nar, nar. I got me some a long time ago. What did ye think I was eatin' all this time? I thought ye were smarter than a monkey, Scurvy Spat!" he laughs and he pops a jelly bean into his mouth.

"But . . ." you want to tell him that it can't be true, because his breath is still bad, but it seems he knew that's what you were going to say, and he leans in so close you can feel his warm, moldy breath on your face.

"Ye think it still bein' bad, aye? Ye should have smelled it before! Breath so vile it be the killer o' many!" he grins, and then bursts into laughter. "Nar, nar, me breath was ne'vr the princess o' the story. It always were me monkey mates."

"But, why didn't you just give them some of your magic beans?"

"Because monkeys be needin' magic bananas, not magic jelly beans. If anyone other than a human be eatin' one o' these" – he held up one of his jelly beans – "it creates a terrible stink."

"So, that's what happened to Monkey Martin, Morgan, and Morta."

"Remember how thay didn't care about how bad thay be smellin' t' th' rest o' us? Thay were nev'r interested in finding a cure t' their problem; it never became an Act o' Villainy fer them. What do ye think would have happened if I told them we be on a quest fer magic bananas?"

You know. "They would have come here and stolen all these bananas."

"Aye. Those not bein' th' monkeys who be deservin' t' have th' treasure. It be these here that be the princess."

His mention of the princess triggers a question you've had for awhile.

"I've been meaning to ask you, why do you call that character function a princess, if it's not always a girl?"

For some reason, this makes Captain Yogger laugh again.

"Aye. Th' answer be as simple as it be complex. Ye see, th' world took a bad turn when people stopped protectin' and rescuing thar princesses. Ye maybe heard I once were a young prince. It be true. As a young boy, I be hearin' one tale aft' another where a princess be captured by a dragon. In ev'ry story, thar be a brave knight who went t' fight th' dragon and free th' princess. When I were all grown, I be seein' many a soul bein' captured fer real by creatures more furious than dragons. But, avast, thar be no brave knights. If a real princess be ever captured, thar be a long line o' knights waitin' t' go fight fer her and t' receive a reward. But, if th' the thing in trouble be not rich or beautiful or royal, or if thar be no reward, then no knights were t' be found. 'Where are thay?' I asked me mom. But she had no answer.

"Truth be, thar were bein' no Heroes fer the smelly, dirty monkeys tak'n from thar homes an' sold as slaves. No one be callin' a filthy monkey a princess. But I do."

And with that, Captain Yogger leaps into the water and begins to swim around with the monkeys, laughing and splashing water at one another as they toss bananas back and forth. It doesn't take you long to decide to join them.

At one point, you take one of the bananas, but Captain Yogger cries out to you, "Magic bananas are only fer monkeys. Thar be no reason fer ye t' be acquiring a stink." The memory of your old roommates stench makes it easy for you to throw it away.

You jump back into the fun, and after awhile – just like Captain Yogger said – you realize the monkeys don't smell nearly as foul as they once did.

EXERCISE #26: TRANSFORMATION

Transformation: The things that change because of the actions of the characters.

All stories have a transformation. As the plot progresses – and the Act of Villainy is liquidated – the story world is changed in some way, big or small. Things are different at the end of the story than they were in the beginning. This is transformation.

Write the name of one of your favorite stories (book, short story, movie):

_____

Describe some ways that things are different in the end than they were at the beginning.

_____

_____

_____

Transformations are common in nature. A caterpillar can magically transform into a beautiful butterfly. A tiny seed can transform into a mighty apple tree.

List five transformations that occur in the world around us.

Example: Planted seed to mighty tree

1. _____

2. _____

3. _____

4. _____

5. _____

Transformation happens all the time in common, everyday events. Your teeth go through a transformation each time you brush them (from brown and grimy to sparkling clean and minty fresh). Each time you eat, your grumbling tummy transforms from being hungry to being satisfied.

List six transformations that occur in your body on a regular basis.

Example: Hungry to satisfied

1. _____   4. _____

2. _____   5. _____

3. _____   6. _____

Our emotions change all the time! Have you ever been really sad and then had someone cheer you up? That's a transformation too.

List six emotional transformations.

Example: Sad to happy

1. _____   4. _____
2. _____   5. _____
3. _____   6. _____

Relationships often go through transformations, too. Think about your best friend. They were a stranger before you met them, right? But, now you know them well. That's a transformation!

List six relational transformations.

Example: Stranger to best friend

1. _____
2. _____
3. _____
4. _____

Some stories have big transformations. Think of a superhero: they often start off as an ordinary person but by the end they have become a Hero who has saved the world. Another big transformation we've all experienced is being born. Another is when a child grows up and becomes an adult!

List six big transformations. (For help, try and find the transformation that takes place in some of your favorite stories.)

Example: Child to adult

1. _____   4. _____
2. _____   5. _____
3. _____   6. _____

Stories describe transformations. In fact, some people believe this is, deep down, the reason why people enjoy stories so much; they delight in the hope that transformation is possible; if the characters in this story can be transformed, maybe I can be also.

Go through the following sentences and fill in the blanks with words that create a positive transformation.

Example: Billy was very <u>tired</u> after a long day at work. But after going home and seeing his family, he felt much more <u>awake</u>.

1. Once upon a time, Jessica lived with her family in a _____. But one day, Prince Jeffery arrived and took her to be his wife. She left her family to live with the prince in a _____.

2. When Peg Arm Andy was a kid, people described him as very _____. But after spending many years out on the sea, now people said he was very _____!

3. Before the sun came up, the animals in the barn were _____. But as soon as the rooster crowed, all the animals were _____.

4. The old man was really _____ until he drank coffee. Afterward, he was _____ and full of _____.

5. One hundred years ago, there was nothing but _____ in the land. Today, it is a place filled with _____!

When characters are transformed over the course of a story they have what is called a "character arc." They are one thing at the beginning of the story and something different at the end.

On the left is a list of possible beginnings for a character, and on the right are possible endings. Connect a beginning to an ending to create what you think would be a positive transformation.

____ Poor	a. Big family
____ Weak	b. Doctor
____ Child	c. Brave
____ Injured	d. Adult
____ Angry	e. Rich
____ Cold	f. Warm
____ No family	g. Home
____ Fearful	h. Happy
____ Lost	i. Healed
____ Student	j. Strong

Character Arc: The transformation that takes place in a character over the course of a story.

NEGATIVE TRANSFORMATION

But don't be fooled! Transformations don't always go from bad things to good things. Sometimes, a character can be transformed into something worse. They can begin the story happy and strong and end sad, alone, and angry. Look at the connections you just made above and imagine the right side was actually the beginning and the left side was the end. Poor characters!

Fill in these blanks again, but this time, make each one of these a negative transformation.

Example: Billy was very <u>alert</u> after a long day at work. But after going home and seeing his family, he felt much more <u>tired</u>.

1. Once upon a time, Jessica lived with her family in a _____. But one day, Prince Jeffery arrived and took her to be his wife. She left her family to live with the prince in a _____.

2. When Peg Arm Andy was a kid, people described him as very _____. But after spending many years out on the sea, now people said he was very _____!

3. Before the sun came up, the animals in the barn were _____. But as soon as the rooster crowed, all the animals were _____.

4. The old man was really _____ until he drank coffee. Afterward, he was _____ and full of _____.

5. One hundred years ago, there was nothing but _____ in the land. Today, it is a place filled with _____!

As we've seen, transformations can be between positive/negative or good/bad, but transformation isn't limited to this. A transformation just needs to be about change. It can be a change of location (a character moves from one city to another) or a change of jobs (from a cook to a teacher) or a change in a stage of growth (student to employee) or something unexpected (one day the beach is empty, the next it's full of treasure).

Using each word, find a way for this thing to be transformed in a way that is neither positive nor negative.
Example: Drinking out of a cup: <u>drinking out of a bowl</u> (or) <u>dropping a cup</u> (or) <u>buying a cup</u>

   1. Eating a hamburger: _____
   2. Sleeping in a bed: _____
   3. Watching TV: _____

4. Hugging a stuffed monkey: _____

5. Wearing a green shirt: _____

6. _____ : _____

7. _____ : _____

8. _____ : _____

9. _____ : _____

10. _____ : _____

Every story needs a transformation; otherwise it isn't a complete story. In the following section, circle "T" if you think it's a complete story because there's been a transformation, and "F" if there hasn't been any change at all.

Example: There was a grumpy pig. The pig was always in a bad mood. (T / F) – FALSE

1. Everyone knew that Jeremy was the best dancer in school, and at the dance he proved that he was. (T / F)

2. The restaurant was going to close because they didn't have enough money, but after getting a loan from the bank, they could stay open. (T / F)

3. The musician broke the strings on his guitar and had to go buy some new ones. Once he changed his strings, he could play the concert. (T / F)

4. The boy always won every board game he played, and last night, he won again. (T / F)

5. The girl was lost in the forest and tried to find her way home, but couldn't do it. (T / F)

Until a transformation takes place, a story isn't complete. Take all the sentences you identified as false and complete the stories here by creating true transformations:

Example: There was a grumpy pig. The pig was always in a bad mood, until one day, he learned how to smile.

_____

_____

_____

_____

_____

_____

BONUS: Look at the complete stories and compare them to the incomplete ones. Other than having a transformation what else did you notice about them that made them complete?

_____

_____

Characters aren't the only ones who can be transformed. In many stories, there is a transformation in things as well as characters, such as objects, places, rules, societies, organizations, or even the entire world!

Underline the thing that was changed in the following examples:

Example: The man's favorite <u>shirt</u> was sprayed by a skunk, and he had to change it.

1. No one expected the massive earthquake to hit Harpoon Town; it was never able to recover from the destruction.

2. Eric was disappointed to find the swimming pool was drained of its water when he arrived for his swimming lessons that day.

3. When the super villain managed to turn on his mind-control ray, the whole world was under his control.

4. Alana took her dad's precious, mint-condition '64 Corvette out for a drive, but returned it with a dented bumper.

5. After the vote, the formerly pirate-friendly continent of Southern Canmerico enacted a law banning all looting and plundering.

Time to create! Make a list of negatives for the character in the left column, and then a list of positives on the right. Then draw an arrow that connects them (pointing either negative to positive or positive to negative) to create a character arc in that character.

Negative   Positive

_____   _____

_____   _____

_____   _____

_____   _____

_____   _____

Now pick three of the transformations you just made and write a very short story. Use what you've learned to create a character and describe that character's transformation:

1. _____

_____

_____

_____

2. _____

_____

_____

_____

3. _____

_____

_____

_____

ONE FINAL "HEAVE HO!"

Transformations don't just happen randomly; they're caused by something.

What do you think caused the pig in my example to go from grumpy to learning how to smile?
Give three possible reasons:

1. _____
2. _____
3. _____

The Pennysville Pears were a local baseball team that lost every game they ever played. But one day, everything changed, and they went on to win the state championship!
Give three reasons for what could have changed for the team:

1. _____
2. _____
3. _____

David and his brothers loved to play board games together, but one day, David said, "board games are lame," and refused to play them anymore.
Give three reasons for what could have changed his mind:

1. _____
2. _____
3. _____

Moo Moo Cow – the local ice cream stand – was open every day of the summer. But when Missy Monkey and Monkey Monica arrived, they found the doors closed and the windows boarded up.
What could have happened to Moo Moo Cow?

1. _____
2. _____
3. _____

Monkey Moby and his family were about to sit down to watch their favorite television show, "Bananas From Heaven," when all of a sudden, the power went out.

What could have happened to the power?

1. _____

2. _____

3. _____

Ready to get complicated? Read this story carefully and see if you can find a transformation:

Josiah Jones was one of the greatest tour guides in the whole forest and boasted that he could never, ever get lost. But one day while walking around late at night, he slipped on a rock and bumped his head. When he woke up, he couldn't figure out where he was, and it took him a whole day to return home. Once he got back, he denied the claims he got lost and told everyone he'd merely "taken longer to come back than planned."

Was there a transformation in this story? (Yes / No)

Why or why not? _____

Don't worry if you aren't sure. This one is tricky! It depends on whether or not Josiah Jones knows he was lost or not.

Do you think he knew he was really lost? Why or why not?

_____

If he was lost, why did he lie about it?

_____

If he wasn't lost, why didn't he tell anyone he slipped and hit his head?

_____

What was the transformation that took place in him? Write it out in a sentence or two.

_____

_____

_____

SCRATCH YER NOGGIN'

Ready for the big review? Try your best to answer these from memory.

1. _____ are things that are valuable.

2. A _____ represents something. It stands in the place of something else.

3. _____ are all the ways different parts of a story come together.

4. _____ is a problem that causes one or more characters to respond to try and solve it.

5. When a character expects things will go one way and then discovers they're going another, we call it a _____

6. To be _____ is to be something worthy of attention.

7. Characters who are in support of the AoV are on the side of _____.

8. Characters who consider the AoV as a problem are on the side of _____.

9. _____ tells us the time and place where the story takes place.

10. _____ is a series of events that occur one after another.

11. _____ fuels our curiosity; it captures our attention and keeps us engaged.

12. A _____ Hero is someone who resolves an AoV for someone else.

13. A _____ Hero is someone who appears to be the Hero, but is not able to liquidate the AoV.

14. A _____ Hero is someone who resolves a problem that directly affects them.

15. Characters are the story _____: characters are the _____ of every story.

16. _____ describe things. These descriptions give details that define who or what a character is.

17. Every story has a _____, _____, and _____.

18. _____ is the string of events that took place in the past.

19. _____ is the things that change because of the actions of the characters.

20. _____ identify what a character wants.

21. _____ is a way of setting limits and creating focus.

22. _____ define what can and cannot happen in the story world.

23. Connect the character function to the correct definition.

_____ Villain   a. Used to resolve the AoV

_____ Princess   b. Informs the Hero of the problem

_____ Dispatcher   c. The thing being fought over

_____ Hero   d. Sovereign over thing being fought over

_____ Donor   e. On the side of the AoV

_____ Magical Agent   f. Connects Hero to Magical Agent

_____ Helper   g. Character who liquidates the AoV

_____ King   h. Contributes to liquidating the AoV

24. Beginning, middle, end is a way to help you _____ all of the

_____ that happen in a story.

25. What is the value of having a specific setting for your story world?

_____

_____

26. What is a worldling? _____

27. What does a story's "shape" mean?

_____

_____

27. What reveals our desires? _____

28. What does "the stakes" for a character mean? _____

29. _____ describes a character who is not fully Dark, and

_____ describes a character who is not fully Light.

30. Name a story you know well: _____

Identify the following for this story:

    Worldling: _____

    Significant object: _____

    Significant place: _____

    Time: _____

    One rule: _____

    One mystery: _____

    AoV: _____

    Princess: _____

    Villain: _____

    Villain's desire: _____

    Villain's stakes: _____

    Hero: _____

    Hero's desire: _____

    Hero's stakes: _____

    Magical agent: _____

    Events in the beginning:

    _____

    _____

    _____

    _____

    Events in the middle:

    _____

    _____

    _____

    Events in the end:

    _____

    _____

    _____

CONCLUSION

Well, Scurvy Spat, I hope you feel pleased. You should now understand the basic building blocks that make up a story; all together, they make up the Grammar of a Story. This is the end of my time teaching you, but I hope it isn't the end of your time with story.

While I would love it if you gave me a five-banana review somewhere, the best thing you could do to reward my work is to create stories of your own. Write one. Go out and film one. Be poetical. Draw a story. Invent silly new words. Create marvelous characters. Get lost among an archipelago of islands. Don't stop searching for treasure, as long as it is the treasure you really need. Keep on learning and growing and laughing and dancing and making lists of things so when a kraken attacks you later in life (and trust me, they will) you will be able to jump on its back and ride it!

So, go on, create some stories of your own.

CHAPTER AVAST AVAST ARGH AYE AYE AYE

After the monkeys fill themselves to their limit, and gather as many bananas as they can carry, you all return to the single remaining rowboat and start your return trip to the pirate ship.

As you leave the island behind, and you start to get closer to the ship, you feel your heart drop into your stomach.

"The mutinous monkeys!" you exclaim as you draw close to the ship and see the jelly bean thieves have returned before you and have taken over the main deck.

Monkey Morta is trying to steer the ship while Monkey Morgan and Monkey Martin stand beside her and shout orders.

"They tryin' to steal the ship!" Monkey Mackenzie exclaims.

You row harder.

"Relax," Captain Yogger sighs, "she no be sailin' fer them. It be me ship. That thar beauty be loyal t' me."

And sure enough, you realize they haven't moved an inch – making it incredibly easy to catch up.

"Hurry! Let's go!" Monkey Morgan shouts at Monkey Morta.

"I trying! It no go!" she cries.

"What do you mean? Just steer th' ship!"

"I trying! I trying!"

No matter what they do, they can't seem to figure out how to move the ship forward. There still is no sail, and no wind to blow it. Monkey Martin orders the other to go below deck and start rowing. Two oars go out, but even this does not cause the ship to budge.

You've often wondered how Captain Yogger managed to sail such a large ship with no sails. It's a mystery you hope to have explained someday.

As you draw closer, you see First Mate Manfred appear on deck with a sword and face Monkey Martin.

"Hello Martin," First Mate Manfred says, "I see you've returned from the island without Captain Yogger."

"Har! Forget LeFossa!" Monkey Martin exclaims as he clashes swords with First Mate Manfred. "Soon people be knowin' and fearin' me name!"

"You're probably right; your smell is already three times worse than his ever was," Manfred replies casually as he deflects the blade with one hand while covering his nose with the other.

"Don't mock me!" Monkey Martin growls. "I'm going to rule these seas!"

"Maybe you should first learn how to rule your fleas."

You're forced to slow your rowing because you can't help but laugh at the flustered expression on Monkey Martin's face.

"Look! It Capt'n Yogger!" you hear the voice of Monkey Monica cry from onboard the ship. "Cap! Help!"

Monkey Martin calls down to Morta and Morgan and orders them to stop rowing and come back up on deck where they can do something useful.

You row next to the pirate ship and all climb on board.

"Ack!" Monkey Martin cries. "Hurry! They gettin' on!"

Monkey Mackenzie, Mini Mate, Missy Monkey, and Norman Nopants – now recharged and strengthened by the magic bananas – grab swords and immediately surround the mutinous monkeys.

"Ye think ye won," Monkey Martin scowls as he, Morta, and Morgan cluster together, "but we not be givin' up our prize so easily!"

"That's not your prize!" you shout at them. "You're nothing but thieves and liars!"

Monkey Morgan shrugs.

"So? We pirates."

"Enough!" Captain Yogger's voice rings through the air. "I rescued ye from slavers an gave ye freedom. I wanted much more fer ye three, but ye made yer choice. Take a rowbo' and go."

The mutinous monkeys are stunned.

"You lettin' them go?" Monkey Monica asks in shock. "With the jelly beans?"

"I gave them a chance, thay made thar choice. Thay don't belong on me ship no more."

They can't believe their luck and mutter under their breath what a fool Captain Yogger is to let them get away. They crowd together in one of the rowboats with their magic jelly beans.

"Anyone else who be thinkin' thay know bett'r than me," Captain Yogger shouts. "Now be the time t' make yer choice. What'll it be, mates? Me, or th' mutinous monkeys an' thar stolen jelly beans?"

The monkey crew exchanges looks with one another. You expect none will move, but are surprised to see that Monkey M goes and joins the mutinous monkeys.

"Ha!" Monkey Martin smirks.

"Monkey M!" Your mouth drops open. "Why?"

Monkey M shrugs, "Story is cool, yo. But I have better things to do."

It makes you sad to see Monkey M get into a rowboat with the other mutinous monkeys, but there's nothing you can do. He's made his choice.

You watch as the four rebels start rowing away. It seems as though they want to flee as quickly as possible – as if afraid Captain Yogger might change his mind and chase after them – when Monkey M turns around and calls out at the top of his lungs, "Yo! I just remembered something. It's all coming back to me. I remember I heard some humans talk about Yogger's magic jelly beans; they said they would give anything to have one. As I've often found myself wanting everything, I decided I needed to get me some of Yogger's beans to sell to those stupid humans. The only mystery was, how do I get Yogger's beans? Well, I came up with a plot and now you know what it was. Mystery solved, yo."

"What!" you yell back. "You lied to us?"

"Of course, yo. It was so easy. None of you ever tried to figure out who I was. Now, these three stinkers and I will be swimming in banana pudding. Yo-yo!" The three monkeys start hollering with delight.

At that, another monkey shouts, "Can I come with you? I want to swim in banana pudding."

Monkey M waves, "Of course, yo, we have enough beans for everyone. Who else wants to join us?"

You're stunned to see four monkeys dive overboard and swim to the rowboat.

"But . . . but," you stammer, "are you really leaving the captain for some beans?" You are distraught. "Captain Yogger, can't you stop them?"

Captain Yogger turns away from them and faces the sea.

"I wish ye protection," he sighs, "now, take yer beans and get away from me ship."

They laugh to themselves as they pull the new members of their crew into their rowboat and row off, singing loudly to themselves.

You stand next to Captain Yogger, who watches them disappear over the horizon with a look of sadness in his eye.

"It hard werk t' grant freedom," he states, "especially when it be ones ye be carin' fer."

"What do you think will happen to them?" you ask.

Captain Yogger sighs as he says, "It be a long way t' th' mainland. Some might not be makin' it. Some will. Th' thing I be worrin' most about is what thay'll be doing t' each other wince thay discover thar bag no be holdin' one single jelly bean in it."

"What?"

First Mate Manfred slides a large bag filled with jelly beans over to you.

"You switched them?"

"Monkeys be not designed fer jelly beans, so me mates filled thar bag with a more healthsome bean, lima beans."

You look at the rowboat, now far away, smile, and say, "The first day I got here you told me not to forget I was on a pirate ship. I think they forgot they were dealing with the notorious Pirate Captain Yogger Lefossa!"

This makes Captain Yogger smile, swing his arms, and hop around the deck on his two peg legs while chanting, "LeFossa, LeFossa, da big pirate bossa," over and over.

Soon the entire ship joins with him, laughing with delight. You look at these remaining, faithful, loyal monkeys. Once wild, they were now unchained.

Monkey Mackenzie and Missy Monkey haul the rest of the magic bananas on board and pass them out to the other monkeys who didn't come to the island; the delight in the eyes of Monkey Monica causes you to smile. But, you are confused.

"Why are you allowing the other monkeys who didn't make it all the way to the cave on the island to eat the magic bananas? I mean, I know some of them – like Monica – are your favorite, but . . ."

"Did she tell ye she be my favorite? Har har har. No. I be havin' no favorites, Scurvy Spat. Monkey Monica – like many others – be failin' time 'n time again. But she be loyal, an' thar be a chance she may one day see th' island fer herself. Her desire is t' help, and mark me words, when th' bigger krakens come, she may be willin' to fight t' defend this ship, not like them mutinous monkeys."

You guess it makes sense that Captain Yogger would rather have a loyal but unhelpful monkey than a helpful but deceptive one.

"Well, I guess we can look forward to the ship being a lot less smelly now that all the monkeys here are eating the magic bananas."

"Aye. Th' magic banana do wonders t' improve one's smell, but thar be a deeper, lastin' smell that still need t' be cured," Captain Yogger explains, "an' so, we now be off to find th' next treasure – the best and truest, an' th' only way to be free o' all smells entirely. Ye must do th' same . . . in yer world."

His final words catch you off guard.

"What does that mean?" you ask.

"It be time fer ye to head home, Scurvy Spat."

"What? Home?" You don't understand. "You know how I can get home?"

"Aye, of course. Thar only be one way t' go home. Th' whirlpool portal," Captain Yogger points overboard, into the ocean.

"Are you serious?" you take a step away. "I can't do that!"

"Ye must."

"Why? I want to stay!" you surprise yourself with your words. Until this moment, you didn't realize how much you've actually come to enjoy life on this ship.

"Aye. But this be no place fer a human child. Ye belong in yer world," Captain Yogger puts his hooked hand on your shoulder. "Thar be treasure an' magic fer ye t' discover back where ye be from. Take what ye learned from me first mate. Use it, and find yer own story."

You want to protest, but deep down you know he's right. You do miss your family.

"Will I ever see you again?" you struggle to speak.

"Aye, mayhaps ye will," Captain Yogger sighs and looks out at the open sea. "Thar be more t' teach, and much more t' do. I be hopin' our paths cross again."

Your heart sags deep in your chest as you say a tearful goodbye to your monkey friends.

"We going to miss you!" Monkey Mackenzie cries.

"Ha!" Missy Monkey grins. "Spat miss us more, I bet!"

You give them each a hug and turn to face the dreaded plank.

But, before you can step on it, you feel a small hand tugging at your shirt.

"Umm . . ." It's Mini Mate, looking up at you with sadness in his eye. "Just wanted t' say . . . umm . . . yer not so bad, Spat."

"Thanks," you reply, suddenly realizing you're going to miss your silly nickname.

"Take care o' yerself." Mini Mate stretches out his hand to shake yours, but you knock it away and instead pick him up and give him a great, big hug.

"Ahh!" Mini Mate's eyes nearly pop out of his head as you put him back down.

"Keep Captain Yogger safe!" you order in as serious a voice as you can manage.

Mini Mate takes a step back and readjusts his shirt.

"Of course!" he grumbles.

Before you step onto the plank, you look over your shoulder and see Norman Nopants and Monkey Monica, each holding a banana and waving at you.

"We miss you already!" Monkey Monica exclaims.

"Da!" Norman agrees. "Norman also hope you nyet forgot the value of 'N' foods!"

You struggle to hide your smile; you're looking forward to eating "normal" food again.

"Thanks for everything!" You wave back at them all as you step out onto the plank. "And Manfred, thank you for all you have taught me about story."

"My pleasure. Don't forget your life is the best story you get to tell. Make it a good one – for me – all right?"

This causes you to wonder. Can you really use all you've learned about the Grammar of Story to help you live the story of your life? That seems strange, but you've experienced far stranger things on this adventure.

You take a few steps forward and look down at the ocean below you. It's frightening, but you take a deep breath. Captain Yogger LeFossa has proven himself trustworthy; he hasn't led you wrong so far, and you don't think he would now.

"Goodbye, Captain Yogger. Goodbye, monkeys!" you call out one last time.

Then you jump.

The water splashes up beside you, and you suddenly feel yourself pulled straight down by some invisible force. You don't have time to be scared, though, because almost as soon as you're pulled under. . .

. . .you're waking up in your bed at home.

"Was it a dream?" you wonder as you yawn. It feels like you've been asleep for ages.

But wait – you feel something sticky in your hand.

You open it and find a glowing, orange jelly bean stuck inside.

RAISE THE ANCHOR AND SET SAIL

Here is one more opportunity to set sail and tell a story of your own. You can write a story about what happens to you, Scurvy Spat, after you wake up back at home. But, as always, you are free to write whatever you want.

_____

_____

_____

_____

_____

_____

_____

_____

_____

_____

_____

_____

_____

_____

_____

_____

_____

_____

_____

_____

_____

_____

_____